MASTER OF MAHIA

Because she had been stranded in Samoa with no money and no job, Lee had been forced to accept the help of the dour and disapproving Drew Hamilton, who took her back to his New Zealand home and set her to work as his shearers' cook. Now her problem was how to get away from the place and somehow get back to England. Or *was* that her real problem?

Books you will enjoy
by KAY THORPE

HALF A WORLD AWAY
A trip to beautiful New Zealand to search for a
long-lost uncle was made even more agreeable
for Nicola when she met Keith Lorimer, and
in a very short time fell in love with him. But
Keith didn't seem to feel anything but friend-
ship for her; why should he, when in the
lovely Annabel he already had everything a
man could possibly want?

KOWHAI COUNTRY
New Zealand—a beautiful new country, a new
life for herself and her young brother! Janey
was full of the highest hopes—hopes that were
dashed, however, as soon as she arrived. But
the charming Tim Hunter offered her a solution to her problems; at least, she thought it
was the solution—until she met Tim's critical
brother Andrew!

MASTER OF MAHIA

BY
GLORIA BEVAN

MILLS & BOON LIMITED
15–16 BROOK'S MEWS
LONDON W1A 1DR

First published 1981
Australian copyright 1981
Philippine copyright 1981
This edition 1981

© Gloria Bevan 1981

ISBN 0 263 73471 4

Made and printed in Great Britain by
Richard Clay (The Chaucer Press), Ltd.,
Bungay, Suffolk

CHAPTER ONE

LEE was settling Mrs Cartwright in a chair in the pale winter sunshine of the porch when her elderly patient said suddenly, 'How would you like a job as my travelling companion for ten days out to the island of Samoa in the South Pacific?'

Lee eyed her charge in astonishment. 'Me?'

The hooded eyes with their shrewd expression flickered over Lee in her neat nursing auxiliary uniform. 'Don't stare like that, girl! Let me tell you you're being offered the chance of a lifetime, and what's more, you're being paid for it. I only hope you have enough sense to take advantage of the offer. If not, you're a fool—you don't believe I'm serious, do you?'

Lee smiled a trifle uncertainly. 'Oh yes, I believe you!' A small girl with a heartwarming smile, snubnosed face and too many freckles, she looked ridiculously youthful for her twenty years. She also possessed a kind heart that was apt to land her in all manner of awkward situations.

Ten days at the continuous beck and call of this cantankerous elderly woman who had swiftly earned herself the reputation as the most unpleasant and demanding of all the patients cared for at the luxuriously appointed nursing home. The overseas trip she was being offered, Lee thought wryly, would be more in the nature of an endurance test than a summer holiday.

'I chose you specially for the chance to go with me,' Mrs Cartwright was saying in her aggravating, condescending tones, 'you look to me a biddable little thing.

Well, take your time, it's up to you.'

A biddable little thing! Lee's soft lips tightened. Was that the way in which Jeremy had thought of her—Jeremy, who had promised her the world? It was so simple to get the things you wanted out of life, he had told her. All he needed, he had explained in his persuasive tones, was a little capital to finance one or two ventures he had in mind and he would be able to make a fortune so quickly that before long they would be able to marry and travel the world together. Because she loved him, or thought she did, Lee had given him the small inheritance left her by her parents. Then little by little, her own savings had been whittled away until in the end there had been nothing left, not even Jeremy. Lee wasn't really surprised to learn that on one of his frequent trips away from London he had become friendly with a woman some years older than himself, the owner of a chain of boutiques throughout the large centres of the country. Not surprised, only deeply hurt and thoroughly disillusioned. How could she have been such a fool as to trust him for so long? A year had passed since the break with Jeremy, yet the thought of him still brought a sick sense of pain and anger.

That was the moment when she all but turned down Mrs Cartwright's offer then and there. Instead she heard her own voice saying slowly, thoughtfully, 'I'll have to think it over.'

Knowing the elderly woman as she did, Lee told herself she would be stupid to accept the offer of the job as companion to Mrs Cartwright, and yet ... She couldn't help feeling a pang of pity for the frail, sharp-tongued woman who seemed to her to be so very much alone in the world. A woman who was old and lonely, whose wealth could buy her only masses of rings and bracelets and pendants and expensive gowns, never the things that really counted, like friends or a loving family, or just one person who really *cared*. For Lee knew that in spite of Mrs Cartwright's imperious attitude towards the staff, and her domineering ways, she was far more frail and helpless than she cared to admit. Why, Lee wondered crossly, must she recall at this particular moment her friend Ann's frequently voiced assertion: 'The trouble with you is that you're far too sympathetic. Worse still, you persist in feeling sorry for the wrong people!' Unconsciously Lee sighed. Well, maybe it was true, but nevertheless ...

She became aware that the hooded eyes were regarding her closely. Mrs Cartwright gave her jaded smile. 'Now that I'm feeling so much better I feel I need a change of climate, and a South Pacific island with lots of sunshine will be ideal for me to pass the time until I'm really fit again. But I need someone with me to look after me when I'm not feeling my best, someone I can depend on——'

'I'm not a qualified nurse, you know,' Lee felt impelled to explain. 'I was studying for my nursing exams, but my mother ... wasn't well ... and I left hospital to stay at home and look after her.'

'Never mind all that.' Mrs Cartwright waved the words aside with a jangle of gold bracelets on a thin wrist. 'All I'm looking for is someone to go along with me on the trip.' Again she regarded Lee with a mirthless smile. 'You'll earn your money easily. All you need to do is keep an eye on my luggage, arrange taxis at both ends of the journey and check plane reservations at both ends of the trip. Your legs are a lot younger than mine and you'll be able to handle all these things for me.' She shot Lee one of her penetrating glances. 'Ever been out of England before?"

'No.'

'No matter, you look a sensible type of girl to me.'

Lee pulled a face. That 'biddable little thing' still rankled, but Mrs Cartwright, intent on her own plans, failed to notice Lee's grimace.

'I'll tell you what to do.'

I bet you will, Lee thought. Was the overseas holiday she was considering worth thinking about when it meant being in the company of an unpleasant, demanding employer? Then once again the sense of compassion took over. There was no doubt that the widow was far from well and badly needed a companion on what might easily prove to be her last overseas holiday. Bad-tempered, inconsiderate and downright bossy though the older woman was, she had set her heart on the holiday in the South Seas. Aloud Lee told her, 'I might not be able to leave my job here.'

She caught the flash of jewelled rings on bent fingers as the matter was swept aside. Clearly Mrs Cartwright was accustomed to having her own way. 'I had a word with Matron this morning and she's agreed to give you three weeks' leave of absence. She told me the matter could be arranged quite easily, no trouble at all. So what's keeping you from coming with me?' The shrewd eyes studied Lee's thoughtful young face. 'At your age I'd have given my eye teeth for a chance to get out and see a bit of the world.'

But not with someone as cantankerous and difficult to please as you! The next moment Lee noticed the tremor in the beringed hands and her traitorous heart softened. After all, she quite enjoyed caring for ailing folk—well, most of them. She became aware of the strident tones.

'My husband and I spent our honeymoon at Aggie Grey's hotel at Apia. It was a quiet place in those days. I've a fancy to go back to Samoa and stay there again, take a look around the island.'

Lee was endeavouring somewhat unsuccessfully to

picture Mrs Cartwright as a bride on her honeymoon on a romantic South Sea island. Had she after all, she wondered, misjudged her elderly patient? She wrenched her mind back to the strong tones.

'Maybe that was why later on when we had some capital to spare Will insisted on giving aid to the people of the Pacific islands, especially in Samoa. Hospitals, education, all that. I used to tell him he was a sentimental old fool and he'd get no thanks for it, but there was no reasoning with him once he got an idea into his head. So I may as well take a trip there and take a look around—I don't suppose you've ever heard of the island?'

'Yes,' said Lee quietly, 'I've heard of it.' *Had she ever?* Samoa, the dream island in the Pacific where Jeremy had planned to take her when the fortune he was so confident of amassing so quickly had become a reality. Deep in her mind something stirred. Samoa was a name that had come to mean to her blue skies and sun-drenched lagoons.

Mrs Cartwright's tones, surprisingly powerful for her frail physique, jerked her back to the present. 'Believe in horoscopes?' she barked.

'Well . . .'

'Don't tell me! You're a Cancer! You've got all the signs.'

Lee's eyes widened in surprise. 'How did you know?'

Mrs Cartwright gave her mirthless chuckle. 'I've studied it for years—here, you'd better read this, it might help you to make up your mind!' She thrust a newspaper towards Lee and the words 'Horoscope for the week' rushed up to meet her gaze.

'Cancer: An excellent day for making a decision. Add initiative to your plans and you should come up with a winner. You may plan to visit faraway places of interest and make new friends. There is an indication for you unattached Cancer people of the romance of your lifetime.' The thoughts rushed through Lee's mind. The romance of a lifetime! If this was what love was all about, the uncertainty, the pain, the ache of longing for a man she knew to be utterly untrustworthy ... if this was all love was, well, at least she had learned her lesson. She wouldn't fall into that particular trap again, not ever! As to the bit about today being a turning point in her life, maybe one could put up with an elderly woman's foibles and ill temper for ten days. Especially, the sneaky thought crept into her mind, when those days were to be spent amid swaying palm trees and brilliant sunshine.

She glanced up to meet Mrs Cartwright's penetrating gaze. 'Well, have you made up your mind? Good lord, girl, what have you got to lose?'

Lee put the newspaper down. What indeed! Not that that ridiculous horoscope had anything to do with her decision. 'All right, then,' she said breathlessly, 'I'll come with you.'

Immediately, having gained her objective, Mrs Cartwright's anxious gaze changed to a cunning, triumphant look. 'That's settled, then. They tell me there's a travel office just down the street. You can go and see them and arrange the trip. I've written down the dates,' she handed Lee a piece of notepaper, 'you can let your people know when you'll be out of the country.'

'I haven't anyone——'

'You can go in your lunch hour,' the masterful tones cut across Lee's soft accents. 'Don't forget, it's Western Samoa and you must make certain we're booked in at Aggie Grey's hotel. Apia, that's the name of the town.'

And the name of the game, Lee thought ruefully, is

patience. Ten days coping with this woman's domineering, self-centred ways. *What have I done?*

Later that day, in the big staff room where the staff took their tea break, Lee told the other girls who worked as auxiliaries of her holiday plans.

'Holiday? Is that what you call it?' Phyl, a tall dark girl, said with a teasing smile.

'She won't let you out of her clutches for one single minute,' another girl put in.

Lee laughed. 'Jealousy will get you nowhere! At least I'll collect a sun tan out of it.'

'Don't be too sure,' warned Phyl. 'If I know that one she'll keep you in the hotel room all the time!'

Lee hadn't realised, when she had helped Mrs Cartwright down the landing steps from the big jet plane last night, the enervating moist heat of the island in the South Pacific. Now, as she made her way along the broken footpath among the friendly Samoan people with their gay clothing and dignified carriage, Lee's footsteps slowed in an effort to keep pace with the elderly woman at her side. 'Come with me to Western Samoa,' Mrs Cartwright had suggested to Lee, 'and we'll catch up with the sun.' Catch up—they were practically defeated by it, Lee thought as she wiped the beads of perspiration from her forehead, and this was only their first day on the island. All at once she realised the reason why so many of the native population strolled on the other side of the road where towering leafy trees lined the bay, or shaded their dark heads with umbrellas or large leaves.

Slowly the two made their way past small timber stores with dark interiors. They came to churches built in an earlier era and then, unexpectedly, a modern supermarket. A little further on in an open market, natives sat crosslegged near the pavement

wielding woven fans, beside them woven baskets of
taros, coconuts, mangoes, bananas. The crowd was
becoming denser now. There was a drizzle of rain on
the pavement, but the shower did nothing to cool the
hot moist air. Jostled by the throng of Samoan people
and tourists, they made their way through the busy
street. A dark-skinned girl carrying a bunch of ripe
bananas passed them, a small native boy thrust his
wares towards Lee. 'Buy a shell pendant! Only forty
cents. You've got lots of money, miss.'

'Tomorrow.' Lee spoke impatiently, her attention
held by the appearance of the woman at her side.
Surely when they had set out to explore the main
street, Mrs Cartwright's face hadn't had that sickly
pallor, the make-up standing out on wrinkled cheeks.
Lee glanced back over her shoulder. All at once the
blue roof of the hotel looked a very long way away. It
had been stupid of them to venture out in the broiling
heat of midday, she realised now, but her companion
had insisted on a stroll down the main street directly
after lunch and Lee had given in.

'We'd better get a taxi——' Even as the words left
her lips, Mrs Cartwright's frail body seemed to fold
and she slid to the steps of a building. 'A drink of
water,' she gasped weakly, 'get me a drink!'

Lee settled her against a wall as best she could, then
told her, 'I'll get it for you—won't be long!' The next
minute she was running, running, forcing her way
through the crowd, all the time peering frantically into
the native stores. At last, in the shadowy interior of a
timber store, she glimpsed bottles of soft drink.

Inside, the place echoed with the blare of pop music
and Lee had to push her way through the crowd of
young Samoan people ringed around the counter.
Goodnaturedly they gave way to her, eyeing her curiously as she called, 'A drink, please! Soft drink, water,
anything will do!'

The dark-skinned woman on the other side of the counter didn't seem to understand.

'One of those!' Lee had to raise her voice above the noise as she indicated the bottles on a shelf.

After what seemed to her an age the assistant took a bottle of soft drink from above her head. Lee's fingers were trembling as frantically she searched in her purse for her traveller's cheques.

'No, no,' the woman shook her head. 'Talas, have you any talas?'

'Talas?' The argument threatened to go on for ever. '*Please*, someone sick——' Desperately Lee attempted to mime her problem. 'Give me a drink in a glass. I'll pay you when I get some talas.'

'You'll pay for the glass too?'

'Yes, yes, please *hurry*!'

To Lee's horror, the woman searched for pen and paper and began making calculations. 'Glasses are forty talas for six. You want one?'

Lee's hands were shaking when at last she emerged from the store with a glass and a bottle of soft drink. Stumbling over the uneven pavements, she all but fell, running through the crowd towards a knot of people she could see gathered on the street. When she reached the place, however, there was no sign of Mrs Cartwright's inert figure on the steps. There was only the group of Samoan people, their dark eyes sympathetic, the murmur of an unfamiliar language. 'The woman, the old lady who was ill?' she gazed at them stupidly, the raspberry-coloured bottle of drink in her hand.

At that moment she became aware of a Samoan traffic officer, in his neat dark blue uniform who was pushing his way through the throng. 'Are you looking for the lady who fainted on the steps?'

'Fainted? Yes, yes, I am. I went away to get her a drink of water. Do you know what's happened to her?'

'Do not worry,' came the courteous tones, 'a man
took her in his car to see the hospital doctor. You are
with her?'

'Yes. The hot sun . . . we only arrived last night.'

'Very hot. You are English?'

Lee nodded.

'Not everyone can take the sudden change, especially one as elderly as your friend. This is her camera,'
he handed Lee Mrs Cartwright's small Instamatic, 'it
fell from your friend's arm when she fell.' A wide
smile lighted the dark friendly face. 'She will be all
right tomorrow, your friend. A little touch of heat exhaustion, that is all.'

'I expect that's what it is.' But a sudden fear stabbed
her. What if her charge had been taken ill with a more
serious malady, here on Apia in the island that was a
small dot in the Pacific Ocean? The best way to find
out how Mrs Cartwright was was to go and see for
herself.

The pleasant-faced traffic officer seemed to read her
thoughts. 'You would like a taxi?' He signalled to a
passing car.

As the taxi took her down a side street and away
from the main thoroughfare, Lee scarcely took in the
wide, tree-lined streets through which she was passing. She had a fleeting impression of houses set back
in wide grounds, of flowering creepers on gates and
over walls and everywhere the scarlet and pink of hibiscus blossoms amidst tropical greenery. The hospital,
Lee saw as the taxi pulled up on a shady street, was a
long grey stone building. She thrust a traveller's
cheque at the taxi driver and hurried in at the wide
open door and into a cool spacious waiting room. 'Mrs
Cartwright,' she told the young native girl in nurse's
uniform, 'how is she?'

For answer Lee was led into a curtained cubicle

where a Samoan doctor, his face relaxed and friendly, greeted her. 'You are with Mrs Cartwright?'

'That's right.' Lee's anxious eyes appealed to the man seated on the other side of the wide desk. 'Could you tell me how she's feeling now?'

'Heat exhaustion,' he explained in his careful English. 'She will rest here. Tomorrow there will be an examination, but you are not to worry——'

Not to worry! She couldn't tell this kindly doctor the thoughts that were crowding into her mind. She'll blame me for not staying with her when she fainted on the steps. She needed me, that's the only reason I'm here on the island, to see that she doesn't come to any harm, and I let her down. I didn't mean to, but try explaining that to her! Lee bit her lip. 'Could I see her?' she asked.

'Sorry, sorry, she wants to see no one. No visitors, she told me to tell you. Perhaps tomorrow?'

It's just as I thought, the thoughts ran through her mind, she blames me for what happened today. If only I could see her and explain! The doctor, who appeared to have all the time in the world, was waiting patiently, and Lee realised she was taking up his time. 'I see. What time shall I come back tomorrow?'

'You come at visiting hour in the afternoon.' He beamed a wide smile. 'She will feel a lot better then, I expect.'

Lee had a suspicion that what he really meant was that after a good night's sleep Mrs Cartwright might feel more kindly disposed towards the girl who had apparently failed in her duties, right at the outset of the trip. All the way as the taxi took her back to the hotel the refrain echoed in her mind. She'll never forgive me for this. Not Mrs Cartwright, she wasn't the forgiving kind. The worrying thoughts crowded back. If only I'd had the right money for the soft drink. If

only the woman in the shop had understood what I
was trying to tell her!

Back at the hotel Lee paid the taxi driver, then
moved through the open-air dining room and down
the steps. Soon she was following one of the narrow
tracks winding among banana palms and flowering
bushes of ginger and sweet-scented frangipani leading
to luxuriously appointed thatched-roofed *fales*—
huts—half hidden amidst the lush tropical greenery.

The limpid blue waters of the pool she passed were
just what she was in need of right at this moment, she
decided. In her air-conditioned cabin she slipped off
her garments and pulled on a gaily-patterned bikini.
In a few minutes she was plunging into the crisp
coolness of the water. She swam a few lengths of the
pool, then climbed out of the water, to lie face down-
wards on the springy green grass at the water's edge.
Lulled by the warmth of a hot Samoan sun, she felt a
sense of relaxation steal over her, and told herself it
was absurd of her to feel upset merely because Mrs
Cartwright hadn't wanted to see her in the hospital
today. The elderly woman was no doubt suffering
from the effects of jet-lag as well as heat exhaustion.
No doubt tomorrow everything would be different and
she would be glad of company.

Lee had been lying sunbathing for a long time when
all at once she realised that the sun's rays had lost their
intensity. Nearby young Samoan men wearing white
sulus were throwing snowy cloths over long tables set
on the palm-shaded grass and dark-skinned girls with
beaming smiles were advancing towards her carrying
great wooden bowls of food. No doubt, Lee thought,
the preparations were for the evening's barbecue meal.

Back in her *fale*, she took a warm shower, then
slipped into bra and tiny bikini panties. She threw
over her shoulders a thin blouse of embroidered cotton

and fastened around her slim waist a flowing muslin skirt. Then she slipped her feet into white strapped sandals. A faint trace of eye-shadow and a touch of lip gloss was all the make-up she needed in the island heat. Running a comb through her damp curly auburn hair, she regarded her mirrored reflection critically, thinking as always that her round freckled face looked childishly immature. Well, there was nothing she could do about it. She had never taken particular note of the intense sea-blue of her eyes, nor did she know that the dimples peeping from the corners of her mouth lent her face an engaging sweetness.

At that moment the compelling beat of sticks on a hollow log alerted her that it was time for her to join the guests strolling over the grass towards the poolside barbecue. As she went outside and made her way towards the long tables she saw that smoke was rising from a barbecue and, in the dusk, flares glimmered alongside the pool and illuminated the trunks of gently stirring coconut palms.

Lee joined in the long line of guests moving around the laden tables with their bewildering assortment of native foods. Glowing hibiscus blossoms were scattered between wooden platters. There were varieties of salads, locally caught seafoods, shrimps smothered in a creamy coconut sauce, tropical fruit salads in bowls decorated with trailing little purple orchids growing wild in the grounds. Carved bowls overflowed with bananas, pineapples, and colourful mangoes, and for guests who wished to sample coconut milk there were whole coconuts ready pierced and holding a straw. There was coffee and wine. There was, Lee reflected, every island delicacy one could wish for.

Pausing at the smoking barbecue, she was served with crisply cooked chicken and pork while a Samoan girl wielded a fan over the hot food. All at once Lee felt slightly conspicuous among the chattering throng and took her tray to a small round table in the shade of overhanging palms, a little distance from the main body of guests.

At least, she consoled herself a few moments later, one other table besides her own was occupied by a solitary diner. Evidently the man preferred to dine alone, and that was odd, her thoughts ran, because he was attractive, very, in a dark, masculine kind of way. Lee looked again and went on looking; she couldn't seem to help herself. Tall, lean, deeply tanned, there was something about him that held her attention. Was it the dark alive face that gave her the impression that he was someone special? Even from a distance, she felt there was an aura of authority about him. She found herself wondering who he was and why he happened to be dining alone in this holiday resort, a man like that. She didn't know how she knew that he was someone worth knowing, she just had that feeling about him.

At that moment he glanced up and as their glances clashed and held, a little shock went through her, for his icy glance was definitely hostile, no doubt about it! He looked coldly furious with her, a stranger! What could be the matter with him? The explanation came unbidden. Of course, he had mistaken her for someone else, another girl—if there could be another girl in the world with a round face and too many freckles. Had she hurt him somehow, that unknown girl, wounded his feelings or made a fool of him? She must have done something to cause him to regard *her* with that contemptuous glance. Well, she thought, indignantly, she had heard of people falling in love across a crowded room, but taking an instant dislike to a stranger was something else again. To think that a moment ago she had been thinking how attractive he looked—but that

was before his dark face had worn the forbidding
scowl with which he was now regarding her. He had
no need to concern himself, she thought with annoyance, if he had any fears that just because she happened to be alone at the same hotel she intended
forcing herself on his notice ... She only wished fate
would hand her an opportunity to repay him for that
tight-lipped glance.

Gradually the line of guests at the barbecue
dwindled and when the meal ended, a group of young
Samoan men picked up their guitars to send music
throbbing through the flare-lighted gloom. Couples
began to dance on the shadowed grass. They were led
by Aggie Grey herself, a hibiscus tucked in her hair as
she swayed to the native melody. Lee knew that the
owner of the hotel had lived here for many years and
was now a legend in her time.

All but hidden in the darkening shadows of overhanging coconut palms, Lee was watching the dancers
when she became aware of feminine voices and the
next moment fragments of conversation were carried
clearly in her direction. It was not until the second
speaker answered that Lee realised the two girls were
discussing the man seated alone at a table not far away.

'Go on, try your luck! Now's your chance, when the
idea is for the girls to ask the men for a dance. You
said yourself he's the most exciting-looking guy on the
island, even if he does like to keep to himself.'

Another feminine voice, younger, not so sure of herself. 'Exciting looking maybe, but he never glances at
any of the girls who are staying here. He didn't even
see me when I said *Tofola* to him in the lounge this
morning.'

'Maybe he doesn't know the language.'

'More likely he's sticking to his girl-friend back
home. No,' voice number two sounded wistful, 'I get

the feeling that I'd be wasting my time with him!'

'Too late anyway. He's got up to go. No dancing for him tonight. He's not interested in social life, by the look of things. I wonder who he is. Didn't someone say he's a New Zealander?'

'That's right. Seems he runs a vast sheep and cattle station somewhere in the outback. I heard he only arrived here two days ago. He's on the way back from a tour of cattle breeders in England and the grapevine has it that he stopped over here to see a friend.'

'He won't be staying long on a stop-over. Oh well, just my luck—are you going to the native concert they're putting on at the *fale* in the hotel down the road tonight?'

'Why not? Who knows, *he* might be there.'

'I'm not so sure I want to meet him now. He looks to me as though he's had a dust-up with someone, all firm-mouthed and angry-looking.' The voices faded as the speakers moved away.

Lee couldn't have agreed more with the comment she had overheard. How she could ever have regarded that man as someone special she would never know.

She got to her feet and wandered through the darkening grounds and up the steps into the open-air lounge. At the notice board she paused to run her eyes down the list of excursions and entertainments offered to guests staying at the hotels on the island. She decided she would settle for the native singing and dancing in a *fale* at another hotel. First, though, she would try once more to get in touch with Mrs Cartwright. Maybe by this time the elderly woman might be feeling sufficiently recovered in health to want to see her this evening. Back in her thatched-roofed cabin, she put a call through to the hospital asking if she could see Mrs Cartwright tonight.

'So sorry,' the soft-voiced Samoan girl at the other

end of the line sounded genuinely regretful, 'but she says no one to see her tonight.'

'Could you tell her it's Lee, the friend who's looking after her? Just ask her if——'

'So sorry. She tell me if a lady rang to give her that message, not tonight.'

'I see. I'll call tomorrow, then.'

'That would be better.'

Thoughtfully Lee replaced the receiver in its cradle. It was understandable, that message, at least it was if you knew Mrs Cartwright and her irritating, autocratic ways. For surely there could be nothing seriously wrong with her. She pushed the niggle of doubt aside. Tomorrow, when she collected her charge from hospital, they might look around the village for the vividly-printed cotton frocks with their cool butterfly sleeves worn by so many of the women at the barbecue tonight.

Her spirits rose as she went out into the fragrant night air. Flares hidden in tropical greenery lighted up long sprays of orchids and the blood-red blossoms of hibiscus bushes crowded the twisting pathways. Soon she was mounting the steps and entering the big airy dining room with its decor of hanging glass fishing floats and strings of shells. Guests were milling about her, the women in long flowing island frocks escorted by men wearing brightly coloured Polynesian printed shirts and pale slacks.

Lee's swift glance searched the room and saw with a sense of relief that the tall dark man with the icy blue eyes was not among the laughing, chattering throng. She wasn't at all surprised. Somehow she couldn't picture the New Zealand sheep farmer with his hostile glance and set lips as one of the lighthearted holiday crowd, not him!

She made herself familiar with the location of the

hotel further around the bay, then strolled on to the street. Outside the sky was a darkening blue, the sea splashed with lights that ringed the bay, and as she took the road following the sea, she caught the murmur of the surf breaking beyond the reef.

Guided by the groups sauntering ahead, at length she turned down a side street with its uneven pavements, then turned again to follow a rough pathway leading to a blaze of lights ahead. Presently she was approaching the entrance of an imposing modern hotel with a huge swimming pool and spacious parking areas. She had no difficulty in locating the locale of the native concert, where else could it be but in the great *fale* with its intricately carved timbers and sides open to the night breeze?

As she went into the lighted building, Lee was welcomed by a Samoan girl, dark-haired and soft-eyed. A smile, a kiss, then a fragrant frangipani necklace was slipped over her shoulders. Another young Samoan girl escorted her to a table in the front row of seats, close to the open space reserved for the night's performers.

Sipping her drink, Lee was conscious once again of feeling a little conspicuous seated here alone, but of course all that would be altered tomorrow night, when Mrs Cartwright had returned from hospital. Very much altered, she mused wryly.

Behind her she was aware of the murmur of voices as guests were shown to small tables, then presently the lights dimmed and to the exuberant beat of wooden drums, Samoan girls with blossoms tucked in glossy dark hair and wearing flowing island frocks, ran on to the floor. To the plucking of guitars they moved with swaying hips and fluttering hand movements, singing and dancing in the rhythm and style of the Polynesian islands.

When the performance came to an end and the girls ran off the stage Lee was applauding with the rest of the audience when she became aware that someone had slipped into the vacant seat at her side. In the near darkness out of a corner of her eye she caught a glimpse of a shadowed masculine face and felt a quiver of excitement. Those firm lips, that strong chin, were disturbingly familiar, darn him, Why must fate have guided him to her table at the performance? Probably, common sense told her, because there were no other vacant seats in the *fale* for a late arrival. Well, it was bad luck for him being seated beside her. Even if he did mistake her for another girl, he was going to feel mighty embarrassed when she let him know his error, as she would in no uncertain terms, if he persisted in regarding her with his baleful stare.

At that moment lights were switched on and she became aware that he was leaning towards her. 'I thought I'd find you here.' She caught the note of hostility in the deep tones. 'Sorry to interrupt your enjoyment of the show——' but he wasn't at all sorry, she knew by the tight look around his mouth and the cold expression in his eyes. At first sight she might have thought him attractive, but not now, not with that angry accusing look with which he was regarding her.

She was really enjoying her moment of revenge and she took her time over it. 'Before you say any more,' she said quietly and distinctly, trying to keep a triumphant note from her voice, 'you may as well get this clear. You happen to be mistaking me for someone else——'

'I think not.' Even though she knew his triumph was to be shortlived, his compelling stare was definitely unnerving. 'You're Lee, I take it—right?' He shot the words at her like bullets out of a gun, she thought.

'Yes, I am.' She faced the chilliest eyes she had ever

encountered. How on earth did he come to know her name? If this were a new approach . . . the hostility in his expression belied the fleeting thought. Aloud she asked, 'How did you know I was coming to the *fale* tonight?'

His smile was twisted. 'Let's say I had inside information. I was told you'd be out enjoying yourself some place or other and there wasn't much offering around the island tonight—I've just come from the hospital.'

She shot him an angry glance. 'It's Mrs Cartwright, isn't it?' The implication was plain, Lee out enjoying herself while the elderly woman lay neglected in her hospital bed. No doubt he was taking in the empty wine glass, on the table beside her, the flower lei, her own flushed face. A hot tide of anger rose in her and she turned to face him squarely. 'I suppose you're the man who picked her up in the street and whisked her off to hospital?'

'That's right.' She got an impression that he didn't want to waste words with her. She could imagine the interpretation Mrs Cartwright would have given him of Lee's having left the ailing woman to get a glass of water to revive her. No doubt Lee had been accused of deserting her charge at a moment when she was most needed. She could imagine the vindictive tones: 'And her a nursing auxiliary too! I really thought I could trust her!'

'I bet,' she cried hotly, 'she told you all sorts of things except the real reason why I was so long getting back to her when she'd fainted on the steps. She'd wanted a drink of water desperately and I went to try and get it for her. It took me ages—first I couldn't find the shop that sold soft drinks, then when the woman did serve me I couldn't make her understand what I wanted and then after all that she wanted me to pay in talas and I didn't have any currency. It wasn't my *fault*! Whatever Mrs Cartwright may have told you,' she cried passionately, 'I was doing my best to help her.'

His cryptic tone cut like a knife. 'Like finding the time to go up to the hospital and have a word with her.'

Her eyes flashed danger signals. 'I went up to the hospital today, but they wouldn't let me see her—you do believe me?'

'I might have if it hadn't been for the visiting hour tonight, at the hospital.'

'Well, don't believe me, then!' A tide of anger was all but choking her. 'If you're determined to listen to lies, to think that I ran off when she needed me, that I didn't bother about her, didn't even trouble to find out afterwards how she was——'

'Did you try?'

'Of course I did!' she flung at him. 'I keep telling you! I rang through to the hospital before I came here tonight and they told me "no visitors".'

His drawling tone was definitely off-putting. 'The girl in the office at the hospital told me that too, but it's amazing what you can do if you use a bit of initiative. No doubt, however, you preferred to spend your evening somewhere more entertaining.'

'How can you say that!' she cried indignantly. 'It wasn't like that at all!' She never knew she could feel such anger. 'Mrs Cartwright had left a message with the girl that she didn't want to see me tonight, goodness knows why!'

His cryptic smile said quite plainly, 'So you say.'

'Whatever I say makes no difference to you, does it?' she hissed at him. 'You'd rather believe *her*! I don't know why I bothered even to try to make you understand.'

His cool glance made her feel even more angry. 'I don't either. Don't trouble thinking up any more excuses, you're wasting your time!'

Lee opened her mouth, then closed it again. 'Oh! You——'

'By the way,' the harsh tones cut across her incensed accents, 'in case you're interested, I've just taken your friend's gear up to her. She had some idea she might be needing it. I couldn't locate you at the hotel,' again the note of accusation in the low tones, 'so I got the key from the manager and shoved her stuff from the wardrobe into her suitcase. Just in case you were wondering what had happened to her belongings.' His tone said, But of course you wouldn't really care what happens to the old lady, not now that you've got the free holiday you were supposed to earn by taking care of her.

Lee scarcely took in the veiled accusation, her mind was still on Mrs Cartwright's state of health. 'You don't mean to tell me,' her eyes were wide with alarm, 'there's nothing seriously wrong with her? Nothing that will keep her in hospital for some time?'

The deadpan tones flicked across her taut nerves. 'How should I know? That's for the doctors to find out I'd say—and don't try to tell me you're worried about her. She's pretty much alone over here on the island. I take it she trusted you, paid you to take care of her,' now there was no mistaking the contemptuous note in his voice, 'to stick around and keep an eye on her instead of enjoying yourself and opting out the first time things got a bit rough. It's no use trying to bluff it out. You left her flat at the first hint of trouble, and you know it!'

Lee drew a deep breath. 'Is that what she told you?'

'It's fairly obvious, I'd say.'

'No, it's *not*!' The words seemed to come to her lips

without her volition. 'It's all very well for you,' she threw at him, 'to judge other people. If you knew Mrs Cartwright as well as I do——'

'I know she's a helpless old lady who depended on someone who let her down badly!'

'That's not true! If you'd only let me explain——'

'Don't bother. I can judge for myself!'

At that moment the lights in the great open building were extinguished, but Lee, almost beside herself with fury and indignation, scarcely noticed. 'I don't know why I bothered to make you see what really happened,' she hissed. 'You have no *right*——' Her voice, rising out of control, was drowned by the exuberant beat of wooden drums, as a group of young Samoan men of outstanding physique leaped on to the floor. Wearing around their oiled bodies *lava-lavas* as bright as the island sun, they shouted joyfully as they performed their native fire dance.

Her thoughts whirling madly, Lee watched as the men twisted and turned, all the time waving their flaming stakes lighted at both ends. One performer was so close to her that she leaned back on her chair in alarm, feeling the heat on her face as the flaming brand traced a whirling pattern against the darkness. For a moment she forgot her own problems, watching in fascination as the men kneeled on the floor, heads thrust back, back, while the burning stakes were held to open mouths. The next moment she jumped in surprise as a brand fell from a brown hand. In a split second the dancer had retrieved the lighted stake while at the same moment she saw a flame spurt up from the hem of her muslin skirt. It had all happened so quickly that she scarcely realised the danger, until her table companion threw his jacket over her knees, smothering the flame, although she was aware of the acrid smell of scorching material.

Before she could utter a word he had taken her arm and was propelling her swiftly and inexorably through an opening between the carved timber poles and out into the cool night air. Brilliant moonlight, almost as light as day, silvered the palm-flecked scene and Lee found herself staring open-mouthed at the one man in the world she wanted to have nothing to do with, let alone find herself in a situation of being beholden to him.

'Thanks,' she said stiffly.

'Never mind that,' he cut in harshly. 'Are you hurt, or was it just your dress that copped that flaming torch?'

'It didn't touch me.'

'Are you sure?' he persisted curtly.

It was the way in which he voiced the enquiry that sent her spirits rising in anger once more. Just as if he had to ask the question but he wasn't really interested in her one little bit.

'I'd know wouldn't I if I had a bad burn, and I haven't.' She added grudgingly, 'Thanks to you having acted so quickly.'

He made no answer but stood, tall and erect, gazing down at her. 'Do you want to go back in there?' His tone was definitely off-putting as he gestured towards the darkened *fale* where the fire dance was still being performed.

'I'd look a bit silly, like this . . .' She bent to spread her skirt, the hem hanging in blackened tatters where the flame had scorched and seared it. 'And this horrible smell of smoke—I suppose,' she added reluctantly, 'you've got it on your jacket too.'

'Not to worry.' He seemed to be nerving himself to some decision. 'I'll see you back to Aggie Grey's.'

'It's okay,' she spoke guardedly. 'I'm not likely to come to any harm walking back by myself in this quiet spot.'

'All the same——' Even the moonglow couldn't soften his stern face. Clearly, she thought, seeing her back to the hotel was the last thing in the world he wanted to do. Well, that went for her too.

'You needn't bother. I'll be quite all right—don't you understand, I *mean* it!' she cried fiercely, and to prove her words she spun around on her heel and marched away.

Head held high, she hurried towards the entrance. She had no need to turn and glance behind her, she could *feel* his eyes boring into her back. No doubt he was hoping he had seen the last of her.

Anger made her oblivious of her surroundings and she had gone quite a distance down a dark lane before she realised that somewhere on the way she had taken a wrong turning. The area where she found herself appeared to be a sort of Chinatown, judging by the signs she could make out on shop windows set far apart. Surely on her way to the entertainment at the *fale* tonight, she hadn't noticed the Oriental markings on shabby stores. She paused irresolute, peering down the lonely pathway. She couldn't really be lost, and yet—— It was at that moment that she became aware of approaching footfalls echoing on the pavement behind her and some instinct made her hurry on. Now there were no lights to be seen and she stumbled on the uneven pathway. In a panic, she quickened her steps and her heart seemed to miss a beat as she re-alised that her pursuer too was walking at a faster pace. Wildly she looked around in search of a turning. Maybe if she could get off the main pathway she could shake him off. She was running now, conscious of someone close behind her. The next moment she was aghast to see a Samoan dwelling glimmering in the moonglow. She had reached the end of the road and there was no escape. Because there was nowhere now to go she stopped, breathing hard, and a hatefully fam-

iliar male voice drawled, 'What's the hurry? You won't
get back to the hotel that way, you know!'

Lee's breath was still coming in gasps as she swung
around to face him. 'It's you! You followed me!'

He, of course, wasn't at all breathless. He stood
calm and unhurried as if he had all the time in the
world. He shrugged broad shoulders. 'If you like to
put it that way. You'd better come with me and I'll
show you the way back to the hotel, if that's what you
want?'

'Of course it is,' she snapped.

'You could have fooled me.'

She was still trying to breathe normally as he moved
a few paces away, then stood still, waiting for her.
'Well, are you coming with me or aren't you?' Even in
the moonglow she could see a twist of his lips that was
a far cry from amusement.

'I'm coming, but not with you. If you'll tell me the
way back to the main road——'

'Go on to the top of this track, then turn right, then
left, then right again——'

'Oh, all *right*,' she said unwillingly, 'I'll come with
you.' Her head was spinning and she had no intention
of getting herself lost for a second time tonight. She
told herself that since he was here she might as well
make use of him. So she hurried along at his side,
striving to keep pace with his long strides that he made
no effort to match to hers. She was ready for him, she
told herself, if he should start to lecture her in the
matter of her supposed neglect of Mrs Cartwright.
Her soft lips tightened at the thought. *Just let him try!*
He said nothing, however, and they took the lonely
roads in silence.

It had been stupid of her, she told herself crossly, to
have taken a wrong turning. Now that they had
reached the main road she glimpsed the dim outline of
the hotel across the curve of the bay.

They were passing the open street market that was a bustle of activity with trucks of local produce turning in at the entrance, when he jerked his head towards a young Samoan man who was seated beside a woven basket of coconuts. 'He's protecting his stall until morning. I guess they don't trust anyone through the night.'

She glanced up at him sharply. He *would* bring up the matter of trust! But his gaze was inscrutable. She said coldly, 'I'll be all right now.'

'Please yourself.'

Lee hurried on ahead, but before long she found herself wishing she hadn't, she was so aware of him striding along behind her. It seemed a long way to the hotel, but at last she reached the entrance doors and soon she was running down the winding path towards her *fale*. Once inside her comfortable cabin, she slammed the door shut. At last she was free of him. Moving into the other bedroom, she peered into the empty wardrobe. There hadn't been much time to unpack, and now that the expensive suitcases were gone, there was no evidence of Mrs Cartwright's brief stay. All at once she paused, startled by her own reflection in a mirror. Could that be herself? Red banners flew in her cheeks, her hair was blown into a curly mass by the night breeze and her muslin skirt hung in ragged, blackened tatters. No matter, she wouldn't need to wear the scorched garment again, any more than she need see that arrogant New Zealand sheep farmer ever again. It was a thought that gave her immense satisfaction.

Later, lying in bed, listening to the rustle of the palms outside her window and the surge of breakers on the reef, she mused that tomorrow would mean the real beginning of her Pacific island holiday. At that moment she became aware of the overpowering perfume of frangipani flowers pervading the room, and on an impulse she got out of bed, picked up the lei and tossed it into the bathroom, then closed the door with a determined bang. Never again, she vowed, would she care for the perfumed, satiny blossoms, not when always they would remind her of a grim-eyed stranger and an encounter she wanted only to forget—if she could!

CHAPTER TWO

LYING in bed that night Lee couldn't seem to banish from her mind the thought of that man's unfounded accusations. It was all thanks to him, she thumped her pillow vigorously, that she was having a sleepless night. Later, however, she must have fallen asleep, for she awoke to the sound of a chorus of birdsong in the garden surroundings. Through the window she caught a glimpse of blue skies and her spirits lifted. She refused to allow that hateful, hectoring—*good-look-ing*, a tiny voice prompted deep in her mind, but she thrust it away. She wouldn't let him spoil her enjoyment of this tropical island. Ridiculous of her to have taken to heart a stranger's unfounded criticism of herself.

A quick shower and soon she was dressed. The briefest of undergarments, a tan-and-white wrap-around cotton skirt, cool white cotton top, white sandals. A smear of eye make-up, a touch of lip gloss, and she was ready for the day. She couldn't wait to bring Mrs Cartwright back to the hotel. If only, the tiny traitorous voice jeered in her mind, for her to be able to prove to that man how utterly mistaken he had been in his snap judgment of her motives.

On the steps outside her *fale*, two Samoan girls were seated chatting together as with deft brown fingers they threaded fresh blossoms of scarlet hibiscus on to spiked stems, no doubt intended for table decorations in the dining room. Lee returned their wide and friendly smiles, then made her way along the pathway cut through lush tropical growth.

Seated alone at her table in the great open-air dining room, she helped herself to fruit from a platter overflowing with bananas, paw-paw, melons and pineapple. After a cup of fragrant coffee, she returned to her *fale* where she picked up the telephone and dialled the number of the hospital. The line continued to give the engaged signal, however, and at length she decided she would take a taxi and make her enquiries at the hospital. Early in the day though it was, no doubt by now Mrs Cartwright would be fully recovered and anxious to return to the hotel.

Out on the street, the small native boy whom she had scarcely noticed yesterday was waiting at the entrance, his shell pendants thrust towards her entreatingly. 'Only forty cents, miss!'

'Not today.' She made to pass by, but the great dark eyes reproached her.

'You said tomorrow,' the boy complained.

'So I did.' Lee paid the boy and taking the pendant fashioned from creamy shells, she slipped it over her head. 'I'll take another one for my friend.' On this golden morning she felt that nothing could go wrong and Mrs Cartwright would possibly care for the gift. Well, she might.

At that moment a taxi glided up beside her and presently she was passing through the wide, tree-lined streets, to draw up at the long, low building. Yesterday things had gone wrong, but she was sure that today her worries would be over and any fears she had had for the elderly woman's health would be allayed. Indeed, her luck continued to hold, for at the hospital a young nurse greeted her. It was a little early to arrive, she told Lee, but no matter. The doctor would see her right away. Following the girl along long quiet corridors, at last Lee found herself facing the same doctor whom she had interviewed yesterday.

'You want to ask me about your friend?' Did she imagine, she wondered, the gleam of disapproval in the liquid dark eyes?

'Yes, yes.' Lee leaned forward, looking at him across the desk. 'How is she? Is she feeling well again now?'

'She is well.'

'I thought she would be better today!' Lee's face was alight with relief. 'May I see her? I know it's not visiting time just now, but I wouldn't be a minute——'

'That is not possible,' came the tones in careful English. 'She has gone, your friend.'

Lee stared at him blankly. 'Gone? How do you mean? I don't understand. Gone where?'

'She has gone back to England. She decided that the climate here . . . too hot, much too hot. She insisted on leaving at once. There was a plane bound for London leaving early this morning and there was a spare seat. The plane,' he consulted his wrist watch, 'will have left the airport an hour ago. You understand?'

Bewilderedly Lee realised that the interview was at an end and she got to her feet. Something in the measured tones had told her that the doctor didn't think much of the elderly woman's companion. Another man who had been given Mrs Cartwright's version of yesterday's unfortunate incident and who believed her to be guilty of shameful neglect. Lee swallowed. 'She didn't leave any message for me?'

The doctor shook his head. 'No message. Nothing.'

Did he imagine she was enquiring about payment due to her? Lee wondered, and felt the hot colour rising in her cheeks.

In spite of what he had been led to believe something of the shock and distress of Lee's young face must have got through to him, for he added in a kindlier tone, 'Mrs Cartwright left here in a great hurry.

There was just time for her to connect with the plane. You will be all right here alone, there is no need to worry. No one will harm you.'

No need to worry. 'I know, I know, thank you.' She sent him a quick smile. 'I must be getting along.'

She had all but reached the door leading out of the building when the Samoan nurse she had met yesterday hurried towards her. 'Wait, please. Mrs Cartwright asked me to tell you if you came here——'

Lee felt a lift of her spirits. So the older woman had thought of her after all, before leaving the island.

'She said to tell you she had settled *her* hotel bill for the night's stay.' The young nurse couldn't realise the implication of the message, Lee thought, or she wouldn't look so happy, as if she were the bearer of good news. Aloud she muttered, 'I see. Thank you for telling me.'

When she got outside, the taxi was waiting at the entrance gates, the driver greeting her with a beaming smile. Had she told the young Samoan to wait for her? She couldn't remember. Dazedly she got inside, staring with unseeing eyes at green lawns and modern timber homes and the open-living dwellings of the Samoan people.

The real desperation of her situation hit her as she reached her luxuriously appointed *fale*. Her *fale*! She couldn't stay on here. She couldn't afford to pay for her hotel accommodation, she couldn't afford anything at all. The few traveller's cheques she had got at the bank in London would allow her to stay for a day or two longer at the hotel and there were a few talas in her purse, and that was all. Previously it hadn't mattered that she had brought little money with her, the arrangement being that Mrs Cartwright would meet all expenses, hotel, taxis, excursion trips around the island and Lee need only pay for her personal outgoings. Now suddenly it mattered a lot. Her thoughts shifted from one possibility to another as she sought to find a way out of her dilemma. It wasn't as if there would be any employment available to her on the island. Auxiliary nursing, the only work in which she had had any experience, was done by Samoan girls working at the hospital.

She couldn't afford to stay here and—she faced the terrifying thought—neither could she return to England. Mrs Cartwright had insisted on buying one-way air tickets to the island. That way, she had told Lee, she could decide how long she wanted to stay. Now, Lee thought bleakly, the decision had been made, and where did that leave her? She could possibly appeal to the British Consulate, but somehow she didn't think she would get a very good reception. Why should they believe her story when appearances were against her and the doctor at the hospital had been given a different version? There must be a way out, if only she could find it! If only she knew someone here on the island, if only the bank would trust her. But why should they lend money to a stranger, especially a girl who would have a lot of trouble explaining the reason why she happened to find herself in such a predicament? Send a cable back home to England? But she had no relatives who could help her. The girls who she had worked with at the hospital in London? She hadn't known them for long, and besides, they would have no money to spare. Her thoughts milled endlessly, seeking a way out but there seemed no answer to the problem. A terrifying thought came unbidden. There was only one plane a week and that meant she had to stay on here for seven days. With no money? If only she hadn't trusted Mrs Cartwright, if only she had brought money with her, borrowed it, anything. If only she hadn't taken on the holiday offer in the first place!

The next few hours Lee spent by the pool, swimming and sunbathing and swimming once again. To all appearances she was just a guest making the most of the warm sunshine, but all the time the worrying thoughts filled her mind. She *must* think of something, and time was running out!

Most of the guests were away from the hotel, some no doubt exploring the island coast or taking bus tours to scenic spots in other parts of the country. Others might possibly be visiting friends, like that insufferable man whom she hadn't seen around the hotel all day. She knew because she had taken particular notice. Maybe he had left Samoa for his sheep station over in New Zealand. Not that she cared where he was. It was only because of his unforgivable treatment of her that she kept thinking of him.

Think of the devil, she told herself the next minute as a man's tall lean figure approached the pool. She couldn't believe he was seeking her out, not him. He wasn't, she realised the next minute, as with a curt inclination of the head he strode past the girl lying sunbathing on the short grass beside the water. Lee raised her head to watch him move along a shaded walkway and insert his key in the door of a creeper-covered *fale*. The wry thought came to her that he was the only guest at the hotel who had spoken to her— that was, if you could call it speaking. Hectoring, browbeating, lecturing was more in the line of his conversation. She went on thinking about him. He was so deeply tanned that the island sun would have little effect on the mahogany brown of his skin. She wondered who his 'friend' was, the one for whom he had specially broken his trip home to look up at Samoa.

Could it be a feminine friend? A girl whom he treated lovingly? At the thought of the treatment he had meted out to her anger rose in her once again. She didn't believe he was capable of even being polite, not with his hatefully superior nature. Criticising her about matters that were none of his business, and not even true!

A crazy idea shot into her mind, a notion so wild and improbable that the very thought of it sent a tingle of excitement through her. But when one was desperate one would try anything, even to appealing to his better nature—what better nature? He was right here in the hotel, he was undoubtedly not without funds and he might even believe her when she explained to him the predicament she was in. Not believe her about the events of yesterday, that would be too much to expect of him. He wouldn't change his mind once he had made it up, not with that firmly set mouth, but he just might agree to lend her the fare home. The next moment she told herself she must be out of her mind to imagine such an eventuality, but on another level she was thinking, I've got to do something, and soon. There's no one else I can approach, and he did know about Mrs Cartwright. He can only refuse me and it won't cost him anything to do that!

She knew that to delay would mean she would lose her courage to carry through such a crazy scheme, so she pulled on her white towelling wrap, lifted her chin and made her way purposefully along the winding walkway to *fale* number 24.

After she had tapped on the door she was tempted to change her mind, but it was too late. The door was flung open and he stood looking down at her. She raised her glance to chilly blue eyes. 'You!'

It was scarcely a welcome and she wondered wildly what she imagined was her reason for being here. The answer didn't bear thinking about and hurriedly she brushed the dismaying thoughts aside. 'Yes, it's me,' she said quietly.

He inclined his head. 'You'd better come in.'

It was a *fale* furnished in the same way as her own. He said brusquely, 'take a seat.'

'No, thanks.' She faced him bravely. At his hard stare all the preconceived explanations she had planned to give him fled from her mind and she came right out with it. 'Can you lend me the fare back to England?'

'*What?*'

'I know, I know it's a stupid situation to be in, but Mrs Cartwright was taking care of all that——' She saw his face harden and knew she had blundered in mentioning the older woman's name. 'You could trust me,' she heard her own voice rushing on, 'you'd get it back. Honestly, I'd see that you were paid as soon as I could. I'd get my old job back at the convalescent home for the elderlies (but would she, once Matron had been told Mrs Cartwright's version of the Samoan trip?). He had a trick of eyeing her from beneath narrowed lids that was making her confused, damn him. It was hard enough being forced to appeal to him of all people, without his eyeing her in that half suspicious, half mocking way. She drew a deep breath and swept on. 'It was just the way it happened. Mrs Cartwright was paying the fares and hotel expenses and all that, so I brought scarcely any money with me. We both had one-way tickets from England and now that she's left the island——'

'She's left the island?' At last she seemed to have made some impression on him.

'By this morning's plane. The doctor up at the hospital told me this morning. Evidently she decided she'd had enough of the island and just—took off home.'

'And I don't suppose,' there was no mistaking the note of accusation in the deep tones, 'you took the trouble to find out about her state of health?'

Lee could feel the hot colour flaming in her cheeks. How *could* she have appealed to him, this detestable man who refused to believe her even when she was telling the truth? She flung away, furious with herself for having given him a further opportunity to insult her. 'I'm sorry I bothered you,' she said tightly. 'I might have known what your answer would be. You've made it plain enough what you think of me and it's not *true*. It isn't as you think at all!'

'Don't hand me any more lies—what was your name? Lee?'

She said stiffly, 'You know it is.'

His tone was ice-cold and somehow menacing. 'Look, I'll make you an offer. Not the fare back to England, that's a bit too steep, but New Zealand's not that far away. I'm booked on the plane leaving at six o'clock tonight and I happen to know there are still a few spare seats. If you like you can come with me, take it from there?'

'To New Zealand,' she echoed blankly, 'with you?'

'What's wrong with that?' Never had she known eyes so cold and forbidding. 'You were paid to come out to the South Pacific. The only difference is that you'll be going on a bit further, with me instead of with a frail old woman. Travelling companion,' he said harshly, 'that's what you were paid for before, I take it?'

Her thoughts were flying in wild confusion. 'Yes, but——'

'For starters I'll tell you something right here and now! You won't put anything over me! I have no intention of putting up with the treatment you handed out to your previous employer.'

Anger sparkled in Lee's eyes. 'I've no intention of

putting anything over you, as you put it. If you don't trust me——'

'Frankly, I don't!'

Two danger signals flared in her cheeks. 'Why are you making me the offer, then?'

'Shall we say a matter of good public relations?'

'If that's all it is——'

'Right now I'd better put you in the picture in case you're interested in the set-up. Drew Hamilton's the name. I run a sheep and cattle station up country in the North Island.' He bent on her his deep unreadable look. 'There's quite a staff at the station and swags of room to spare at the homestead, so don't look so worried——' His eyes said contemptuously, 'I wouldn't touch you for quids!' 'I'll see that you're fixed up with money. Well,' he sounded impatient, 'it's up to you!'

She stared up into the closed face, trying to take in the implication of his words. 'You mean you'd give me the fare money?'

'*Give* it to you?' Her gaze fell beneath his compelling stare. 'Whatever gave you that idea? You'll earn that money, make no mistake!'

'How,' she demanded, 'will I earn it?' and held her breath as she waited for the answer.

He shrugged broad shoulders. 'No doubt,' he drawled carelessly, 'I'll find something to keep you busy.'

Painfully aware of the telltale colour flooding her face, she said very low, 'You really mean a job?'

'You don't think,' the faint note of contempt in the deep tones stung her, 'that I'd be interested in *you*, do you?'

It was too much. She didn't have to take his insulting behaviour—or did she?

'Forget about the loan,' she said stiffly. 'I'm sorry I bothered you.' She turned away.

'No bother.' The cool tones halted her as she moved towards the door. Just as if she hadn't spoken, he was saying matter-of-factly, 'I'll get on to the travel people and get your air ticket fixed up for tonight then, okay?'

She turned to face him. 'But you still don't trust me to pay the money back?'

'Trust you?' His eyes were flint. 'Don't worry, I'll see that you do! I scarcely think you'll find me such an easy mark as a poor frail old woman——'

'Poor old woman my foot! I keep telling you——'

'You're wasting your breath.' He was taking a wallet from the hip pocket of his shorts. 'You'll need some funds, I take it, to settle the hotel bill——'

Lee lifted her chin defiantly. 'I need a *loan*!'

'Make it five hundred dollars, then,' and as she caught her breath, 'don't worry, I can take it out of your wages if that makes you feel any better about it.'

Reluctantly she took the wad of notes he was holding out to her. 'You'll get it back.'

He gave a short laugh. 'I'll make sure I do.'

'Doing what?'

It was ridiculous, she thought, he hadn't even specified what her duties were to be. What did an English girl do for a living on a New Zealand sheep station?'

'You'll find out when we get to Mahia. There's one thing for sure, though. There won't be any frail old ladies needing your attention.'

She gasped. 'You—you never let up on me, do you? I've half a mind——'

He cut in smoothly in his maddening drawl, 'Now we've got that settled I'll see about getting you an air booking for Auckland. With luck, there'll be a seat to spare.'

'Lucky? For whom?'

A sardonic smile curved his lips. 'I take it you won't take it to heart if I can't book two seats together?'

Lee was so angry with him she could have hit him.

'How did you guess?' she flung at him, and hurried towards the door.

The interview with Drew Hamilton had shaken her more than she cared to admit, she realised a little later as back in her *fale* she began pulling garments from the wardrobe and folding them in readiness for packing once again.

There was no need for him to have made me feel so damnably indebted to him. She jerked a hanger from the wardrobe. He was positively revelling in getting me at his mercy. I bet he'll go on being that way—another angry jerk at a hanger—until I manage to save up enough money to pay the fare back home, and goodness knows when that will be! All at once a thought assailed her. Would her light garments be suitable for the New Zealand summer? Wasn't the climate cooler than here? No matter, her clothing would just have to do until she could shop for something else, that was if there were any shops where she was going. Suddenly she realised how little she knew of her destination. Her hand stilled on the key she was turning in the lock. For that matter, what did she know of Drew Hamilton? Only that he was hard and arrogant and insufferably autocratic, lean good looks notwithstanding. The thought came unbidden that apparently she had exchanged one demanding boss for another and it wasn't funny, it wasn't funny at all.

The jangling of the telephone bell startled her from her musing. There was only one person in the hotel who was likely to ring her, and at the thought of him she felt the hot anger rising once again. Picking up the receiver, she forced her voice to a steady note. 'Yes?'

'Lee?' He didn't wait for an answer. 'You can relax.' Relax! Thank heaven he couldn't know that her hand holding the receiver was trembling violently. It was the way he affected her. She wrenched her mind back to the deep masculine tones. 'I've just been on the blower to the travel agency and it seems you'll be all right for tonight's trip.' Nothing could have been more impersonal than the curt accents. 'Pick you up from here at five o'clock, right?'

'I'll be ready.'

She was ready and waiting later that day when a knock sounded on the door of her cabin. Tall and dark and incredibly attractive for such a horrible person, Drew Hamilton acknowledged her with a barely noticeable inclination of his head, then his glance moved to her modest suitcase. 'I'll take that.' He picked it up, then hesitated. 'You've settled the bill with the manager?'

Lee's soft lips tightened. 'Of course I have. What do you take me for?'

His shrug of broad shoulders answered her question in a way that was anything but flattering. He made her so furious! 'You don't think,' she flung at him, 'that I'm dishonest as well as——'

'I thought you might have forgotten—shall we go?' They moved along the tropical walkway together, her expression stiff and resentful, his closed face giving nothing away.

She hurried along beside him, endeavouring to keep pace with his long strides. 'I know you've had to pay the plane fare to New Zealand, but I'll pay it back as soon as I can. I'd have enough to cover it from the amount you loaned me.'

'Forget it. We'll settle up later.'

Some devil of resentment prompted her to say impishly,

'If I stay.'

'There'll be no question about that.'

What on earth did he mean, Lee wondered, and what on earth had she let herself in for? She was

searching her mind for a suitable retort intended to
show him that she had no intention of being pushed
around, even if she had been forced into an arrangement with him. At that moment, however, they gained
the street and a small car drew up beside them. A gay
voice called, 'Anyone for the airport?' and an attrac-
tive-looking young woman leaned across to fling open
the passenger door. Lee thought that Drew Hamilton
looked slightly discomfited at the unexpected encounter, but that would be because he had her in tow.
He said, 'I told you not to bother.'

'Did you?' The stranger had a merry laugh. 'I
didn't hear anything of that. Hop in!'

So this, Lee thought, was the 'friend' on whose
account Drew had made a special stop-over on his way
back from England. Judging by the girl's appearance,
everything about her was cool and fresh even in the
humidity of the island, and that low, provocative
voice—no wonder he had broken his journey at
Samoa.

'Beverley, this is Lee, she's taking off on the same
plane.'

Even though it must have cost her an effort, Lee
mused, the girl's voice was as gay and welcoming as
ever. 'You won't mind the back seat?'

Lee much preferred it, but she merely smiled and
got in the car while Drew stowed her luggage in the
boot.

The winding road to the airport was much more
interesting than she had realised on her arrival in the
darkness. Now she could see that the route followed
the coast, passing open *fales* where the Samoans lived,
each timber dwelling open-sided and festooned with
purple bougainvillea or decorated with bunches of
fresh flowers. Everywhere was warmth and colour and
hot sunshine. The friendly dark-haired girl kept up a

flow of animated conversation that Drew answered in a few words. No doubt the silent passenger in the back seat was scarcely conducive to intimate conversation. Lee was oddly pleased at the thought. He deserved it. He wasn't going to have things all his own way!

When they drew up at the airport they checked in at the counter, then took their place among the crowd of people milling around the barrier. When at last their plane arrived and it was time to get aboard, Lee turned enquiringly towards Drew. At that moment the other girl reached up to kiss him. The next minute he had turned away and he and Lee were moving over the tarmac, the wind tossing his black hair back from his forehead and whipping Lee's cotton skirt around her legs.

After showing Drew to a seat on the plane, the air hostess led Lee further down the narrow corridor. Had Drew made certain, she wondered, that he wouldn't be lumbered with her all the way to Auckland? She wouldn't put it past him. Indeed it would be quite in line with his opinion of her.

She could see Drew further along the compartment. He had taken a paperback from his jacket pocket and was already reading. Clearly he hadn't the slightest interest in her whereabouts on the plane. He wasn't interested in the friend who had driven them to the airport either, she mused, watching the girl who stood waving from behind the barrier. Drew looked up, sent her a desultory lift of a tanned hand, and that was all. The next moment the engines roared, the plane rushed down the runway and soon they were airborne, looking down over coconut plantations and softly-curling surf, then there was only the deep turquoise blue of the Pacific Ocean far below.

The meal served on the plane was tastefully prepared and attractively served, but Lee picked at her

plate; somehow she felt on edge, waiting for she knew
not what. Yet it was surprising, she mused a little
later, how the time sped by. Could it be because she
dreaded what the future might hold for her that the
journey didn't drag and it seemed only a short time
until, through the plane window, she glimpsed far
below the lights of Auckland city—handfuls of
jewelled necklaces flung on the dark velvet of the
night. Then they were sweeping down and reluctantly
Lee fastened her safety belt in preparation for landing.

As the plane slowed to a stop and the passengers
began to collect their belongings she could see Drew's
tall figure advancing towards her. He came up and
placed a hand on her arm to guide her along the exit
passageway. Just as if he owned her, Lee thought
angrily, and shaking off his hand she stalked ahead,
head held high. The thought ran through her mind
that if she weren't careful she would come to hold her
chin permanently up in the air, but she had to prove to
him that lending a girl money didn't entail owning
her, as he would very soon discover.

She was waiting at the Customs barrier when he
joined her again.

'We're through,' he said, 'no problems. Come along,
I'll get a car and we'll be on our way!'

She had to admit that he appeared to organise transport without apparent effort—but no doubt it was
easy, she told herself, when all he had to do was to
stop at the rental car counter of the airport and pull
out his cheque book. From what Lee could make out,
he was arranging to leave the car at the nearest town
tomorrow. Strange how politely he was speaking with
the rental car girl attendant, and how horrible he had
been to her. It seemed that he could make himself
agreeable to other girls, anyone except her. Not that
she *cared*, of course.

CHAPTER THREE

As she went with Drew into the airport lounge Lee found herself facing a battery of strange faces, all eagerly scanning new arrivals in the hope of finding friends and relatives arriving on the plane from the Pacific islands. Soon they were outside in the cool night air where a yellow rental car awaited them. Drew tossed the luggage into the boot, then saw Lee settled inside. She seated herself as far away from him as possible, but he made no comment. The next minute his hand was on the starter motor, he slipped the car into gear and they were moving away from the airport and taking a smooth road cutting between farmlands. Presently they swung into a southern motorway leading, Lee reflected uneasily, to goodness knows where. All at once she was swept by panic. She was risking everything on the promise of a stranger, a man who despised her. It was a crazy situation. Yet the odd thing was that in some inexplicable way she trusted him to keep his word to her.

But later, deep in the loneliness of the countryside, the worrying doubts came crowding back to mind. What did she really know of him, this cool-eyed stranger? Unconsciously she found herself offering up a little prayer. 'Make it all right. *Please* make it all right!'

It was a silent journey through the night. Drew appeared to have nothing to say to her and she wondered if he were already regretting the impulse that had prompted him to extend a helping hand to a strange girl whom he couldn't stand to have around. Lee let the silence grow; what did it matter? When he had spoken to her it had been only to lecture her in his arrogant way on matters of which he was completely misinformed. So she pretended sleep and must indeed have dozed off into slumber, for she awoke with a start to find herself curled peacefully against his shoulder. With a muttered 'Must have fallen asleep' she flung herself back to her corner of the seat and stared out into the darkness.

Drew was a good driver, she would give him that. At least that was one hazard she need have no concern about in this strange journey through the night. In an effort to brush aside her apprehensions she asked, 'What time is it?'

'Going on for midnight.' His gaze was fixed on a bend ahead.

'Midnight?' She sat up straight. 'It can't be!' Why, she must have slept for an hour or even longer. 'How far is it now?'

'We've not passed the half way mark yet, not by a long shot. There's a stopping place coming up in five minutes.'

'Stopping place?' She wondered what he meant.

The deep impassive tones supplied the answer to her query. 'I usually break the trip on this run around here. It's the last place where you can find accommodation. No sense in pushing on through the rest of the night and risking falling asleep at the wheel.'

'I couldn't imagine your doing that!' The words came unbidden. Not him, so much in charge of the situation. Too much so, when it came to her own affairs.

He ignored the personal comment. 'One more bend—here we are!' A lighted building loomed into view and he drew up beneath a sign outlined in lights, 'Roadway Motel'. 'Even if they happen to have a full house, they won't turn me away.'

They probably wouldn't dare! But she made the observation silently.

'Wait here,' Drew had climbed out of the car, 'and I'll have a word with the owner.'

She watched him stride up the path leading to the building and presently he was pressing a finger to the doorbell. The door opened and she could see the two men speaking together. Was the motel fully booked up after all? She almost wished it were, if only to show him he couldn't order the whole world around to suit himself. He wasn't all that omnipotent, even though he might like to give that impression.

The next minute he was back at the car, taking the bags from the boot, opening the door for her to get out. 'We're all right! Seems there's a Rugby game on here tomorrow and they're chock-a-block, but I persuaded him to fit us in.'

A terrible suspicion shot into Lee's mind. 'Fit us in?' she echoed in a guarded tone. 'How do you mean?'

'It's a bit inconvenient,' they were strolling towards the open doorway ahead, 'but it's the best I could manage. It's either this or nothing. It's only a single unit, but I was darn lucky to get it.' He didn't appear to notice her gasp of surprise. 'At least we can bed down for the night.'

Did he or didn't he realise what he was saying? Blithely chatting on, expecting her to fall in with his plans. Plans?

'Look, before we go any further,' she paused on the pathway, danger signals flaring in her eyes, 'I'd like to get one thing straight——'

'Two single beds—*two*,' he bent on her his cold, contemptuous stare. 'You've nothing to fear from me. It's a long drive to Ahauri, I need a break, and this is the last stopping place on the road, so unless you prefer to sit up in the car for the rest of the night . . . I can assure you it's all the same to me.'

The angry note in his tones was reassuring and Lee decided to throw it over to fate. Wasn't that what this new life of hers was all about, taking chances, hoping things would work out in the end?

'Are you coming in, or going back there?' Drew jerked his head back towards the car, the ignition keys jingling in his hand.

To hell with him, she thought, and aloud, 'I'm coming.'

The proprietor of the motel, a chubby tanned man of middle age, welcomed them inside. He showed no surprise at meeting Lee and she wondered how Drew had explained her presence here. The eager way in which the man hung on Drew's words told her that the motel owner thought a lot of this back-country sheep farmer. At last they were shown into an immaculate unit and the proprietor wished them a good night—what was left of it.

'I could use a drink right now.' Drew was filling a chrome jug with hot water at the shining sink, then taking down beakers from the shelf. He opened a cupboard, searching for coffee powder, and Lee took the opportunity of glancing into the adjoining bedroom with its two single beds. Drew was spooning instant coffee into pottery beakers when he paused to glance up enquiringly. 'Milk? Sugar?' Fortunately, she thought, he hadn't caught her furtive glance into the next room.

'Milk, please.'

'This will make you feel better.' Did it show so much, she wondered, the apprehension she was feeling? It was all very well for him, she thought crossly, he wasn't the one who was forced to take chances! She sipped her coffee slowly, making it last as long as she possibly could, but at last even the king-sized beaker was empty.

Drew rose from the table, lazily stretching his arms. 'Do you want the bathroom first?' He seemed entirely unconcerned, but then, she mused bitterly, he could afford to be. 'It's okay,' she made her tone as nonchalant as she could, 'after you.'

When he came out of the bathroom, dark hair damp from the shower, she had washed the beakers and put them away.

She let the shower run a long time, but in the end she had to come out. By the light shining from the diminutive kitchen she saw that the bedroom was in darkness and a glimpse towards the bed by the far wall told her that Drew was already there. Swiftly she switched off the light, slipped off her outer garments and a moment later she crawled between the sheets. For a long time she lay there tense and stiff, and it wasn't until Drew's even breathing told her that he had fallen asleep that gradually her taut muscles relaxed.

When she awoke in the morning the twin bed was empty and she caught the hum of an electric shaver from the bathroom. She pulled on her clothes, then went to peer out of the window, where a brilliant flush of bright pink heralded the sunrise. All around was a sea of brown tussock. It was unfamiliar country, the first day of a new life! All at once excitement flooded her and out of nowhere the horoscope forecast flashed back to mind. Even perhaps, according to the reading, a new love? Who knows, she mused, maybe at Mahia, wherever that might be, here at the ends of the ends of the earth, he'll be waiting for me, the love of my lifetime! Silly to take a horoscope reading seriously, but all the same it was . . . interesting. Meanwhile, she ran a comb through her hair, then went into the kitchen. As she switched on the electric jug and poured cereal into bowls she mused on all the travellers who had broken their journey here. There surely could never have been a more ill-assorted couple sharing this unit than Drew and herself, a man and a girl who sparked in each other an instant antagonism. And here she was busily preparing his breakfast!

A few minutes later Drew came to join her. With a cool ' 'Morning' tossed in her direction, he seated himself opposite her at the small table. He wasted little time on the meal, downing a quick drink of coffee and buttering a slice of toast. Was he in haste to reach his home after a long absence? she wondered. More likely he couldn't wait to free himself of her unwanted company! She herself had little appetite, alone here with him, and it was with a sense of relief that she rose from the table. While he settled the bill she wandered towards the door.

Outside in the incredibly clear air, Lee stood motionless, her personal problems dwarfed by the sight of a majestic mountain, its snow-capped peaks rising against a cloud-filled sky.

He came to stand at her side. 'That's Ruapehu. You're in snow country now, Tongariro National Park.' He spoke tersely as if only common courtesy impelled him to volunteer the information. 'Take a look at the other mountain,' he gestured with a lean, sun-bronzed hand, 'it's a volcano.'

As Lee's gaze lifted to a symmetrical shape soaring into the clouds she caught her breath in wonder. Dark blue against the sun, a plume of smoke billowing from the summit, the snow-streaked slopes reached for the sky.

For a moment she forgot who she was with, and cried impulsively, 'There's a cloud of smoke coming from it!' Her eyes widened in apprehension. 'It won't blow up, will it?'

'Hardly. Though it's always on the cards. You never can tell what can happen when it comes to volcanoes.

Old Ngaruahoe's been belching out smoke and ash and tossing the odd rock down the mountainside a lot lately, just to show it's still alive and kicking. The geologists keep a wary eye on it, but you don't need to worry. It's been playing up on and off for years!'

Back in the car he reverted to the discomfiting silence of the previous day. Could it be he was regretting having spoken to her as if she were any travelling companion on a long journey, instead of—she shied away from his opinion of her.

It was the longest day she had ever known. The small townships through which they passed broke the monotony of the journey that seemed to Lee to consist of endless miles of hill country followed by river flats where sheep and cattle grazed.

Once on a lonely slope she caught sight of a shepherd with his dogs, black steers huddled in the shade of a clump of cabbage trees. So this, she mused, was the New Zealand outback. If this were the type of country for which she was bound, she had better like the life, for it seemed a very long way back to civilisation. They were high in the hills, climbing a steep slope, when she raised her glance to the masculine profile at her side. 'Where is it, your home?'

'Mahia? Coming up right now!' The next moment they reached the summit and he braked to a stop. 'From here you get a sort of plunging view——' He had forgotten her, she knew, his face alight with emotion. Was it pride, excitement? She couldn't tell. Her gaze went down the slopes where station land tumbled down to meet the white-flecked blue of the Pacific Ocean.

'You're in luck seeing it like this, there's usually a hell of a wind blowing, but today——' She saw his expression soften. 'That's it!' His tone rang with pride just as if the old green-roofed station building nestling

among poplars far below was the only place in the
whole world worth living in. Perhaps it was, to him.

There was a silence, only it wasn't an uncomfortable
silence this time. Curiously Lee gazed down the
rugged cliffs where sheep grazed. Why, it's like a small
township, she thought, taking in the old gabled homestead in its shelterbelt of poplars, the mellow red of
stables, a cluster of outbuildings. 'What's the long low
building?'

'That's the woolshed, where it all happens.' Clearly
he had forgotten her or he wouldn't have spoken with
so much enthusiasm. 'Over there behind the fence,
those are the shearers' quarters, the two cottages are
for the married shepherds and that little timber place
near the homestead is the old school.'

She was startled. 'A school on the property? Are
there so many children to attend it?'

'Not at the moment. The four kids who live on the
station are on correspondence work, but the old place
has had plenty of use. When I started there as a kid,
this road was only a clay track, cut off from the interior. You couldn't get through to the homestead in
winter and all the wool had to be sent away by sea.' He
started the motor and they took a track that zigzagged
down to sea level, the salt tang of the wind in their
nostrils.

Lee thought the outback station was fairly remote as
it was. Yet despite her apprehensions she felt a height-
ened sense of awareness as they swung down to the
flat and took a winding driveway leading to the homestead. As they swept past the stables a man looked up
from saddling his horse, his expression of mild surprise changing in a twinkling to one of disbelief, then
astonishment. Clearly, Lee thought, the boss wasn't in
the habit of bringing a strange female back with him
from an overseas trip. Humiliating to think she had

wished herself on him. She drew him a quick sideways glance, but beyond a hand lifted in a salute and a friendly grin, Drew appeared oblivious of his stockman's surprised expression.

For the first time Lee wondered how Drew was going to explain her arrival at the house. Somehow, in spite of his low opinion of her, she couldn't see him confiding to his family the true facts of their brief acquaintance. That was, if he had a family. How little she knew of him, nothing at all really.

As they swung past the woolshed and turned into the winding driveway leading to the homestead, Lee's gaze went to a long verandah running the length of the house where two feminine figures leaned over the railing, both waving enthusiastically to Drew. The older woman was tall and slender with greying hair cut short. She wore a loose checked overblouse and slacks and looked to Lee to be blessedly ordinary-looking. Somehow today she couldn't bear to be faced with a supercilious female, not with all the other problems she had to contend with in this new, untried existence. The other one—Lee did a double-take, for as they drew up below the flight of steps leading to the porch, she could see that the young girl waiting to welcome Drew to his home was really something. The smooth blonde hair and make-up were flawless, the dress a fashion model, and her smile was all for Drew.

'Drew—darling!' He had scarcely set foot on the steps when the vision came running towards him and threw herself into his arms. Nestling against his shoulder, she glanced up at him. 'I thought you were never coming back!' She pouted prettily. 'Why did you stay away so long?'

Gently he disengaged the clinging arms from around his neck. 'Knock it off, kitten.' Over the blonde head his glance went to the older woman who was now descending the steps. 'Hi, Mum! How are things?'

'Better now that you're back!' Lee liked her at sight, this middle-aged woman with the tanned skin untouched by make-up and clear eyes. Eyes that said quite plainly to her son, 'Who is she?'

As they mounted the steps together he said carelessly, 'I brought Lee along to stay for a while.' The way he spoke of her, Lee thought resentfully, she might just as well have been a sheepdog puppy he was transporting to his home. She wrenched her mind back to the vibrant, masculine tones. 'Lee—my mother.'

Lee put on her brightest smile, but inwardly she was aware of the silence.

'We met up in Samoa,' Drew added carelessly. 'We both happened to be putting up at Aggie Grey's hotel.'

To Lee the words gave a misleading impression of their relationship and she glanced wildly towards Drew to put matters right. He appeared, however, to be scarcely interested in the matter. 'Lee comes from England. She'd never been out of the country before, so I told her that seeing she'd got as far as the Pacific islands, she might just as well come out to Kiwiland and take a look around, get an idea of the outback. I told her we had swags of room.'

'Of course,' the older woman said in a slightly puzzled tone, and once again the thought shot through Lee's mind that clearly Drew wasn't in the habit of bringing home strange females.

Lee was uneasily aware of the other girl, whose gaze was moving from Drew to Lee. Lee could almost *see* the suspicions forming behind the great brown eyes. Who is she really? Why is he bringing her here? Why does she seem so embarrassed over the visit?

'This is Katrina, Lee,' Drew was saying. 'She's not

exactly a visitor, more like one of the family, a cousin——'

'*Second* cousin,' Katrina corrected him in her sweet, childish tones. 'There's quite a difference.' Her pouting gaze swept up to Drew's face. 'Being a second makes things much more interesting.' She shot Lee a look from under her lashes. 'How long can you stay, Lee?'

The question hung in the air. Lee's gaze flew to Drew. 'Over to you,' her glance signalled.

Her thoughts were whirling. Would he or wouldn't he explain the real purpose of her visit? Visit? It promised to be an endurance test, judging by the implacable look in his eyes.

He said in his lazy drawl, 'Oh, I guess Lee'll be around for a while. She wants to have a look around a sheep station before she goes back to England.'

She let out a breath of relief. At least he had let her off the hook so far as his family were concerned. She couldn't help the thought that judging by Katrina's suspicious attitude, the other girl would have been delighted had she been made aware of the true circumstances that had brought her here. If Katrina only knew, she thought wryly, the other girl had nothing to fear from her!

'Come along inside. You're very welcome to stay as long as you like.' Drew's mother's friendly smile made Lee feel more than ever an impostor, but she went with the others through a wide vestibule decorated with great bowls of fresh flowers, and down a carpeted hallway. 'It's just as well we have lots of room,' the older woman said to Lee, 'we never know who's going to arrive here unexpectedly. Stock agents, campers who've lost their way, salesmen with car trouble——'

And me. But Lee made the observation silently. She was sure that when it came to unexpected guests,

Drew would have put her at the tail end of the list.

As they went up the stairs Katrina, clinging to Drew's arm, talked incessantly and Mrs Hamilton's low modulated tones were in contrast to the girl's high childish voice and frequent bursts of laughter.

'I'll put you in the blue room.' Drew's mother flung open a door off the hall. 'It's a long trip by road. You'll be feeling like some lunch by this time, but I expect you'd like to freshen up first. The bathroom's along at the end of the passage.'

'Thank you.'

Drew flung her suitcase down on a low table, then left the room with Katrina. Lee could hear the girl's high sweet tones echoing from the hall as the two moved away.

'It's a lovely room,' Lee told her hostess, thinking how bright and welcoming was the bedroom with its soft blue walls and gay mauve and blue printed linen bedcover and curtains. The furniture was old and satin-smooth and creamy sheepskin rugs lay on the stained floor.

'It's comfortable, put it that way.' Mrs Hamilton crossed the room to fling open french doors, sending white nylon curtains billowing in the salty breeze and letting in a vista of steep hills rising almost vertically from sea-level. 'Come along to the dining room when you're ready. We've waited lunch for Drew, seeing he's been away from home for over a month. You've no idea of the problems we've had to contend with while the boss was away!' Grey eyes twinkled in a tanned face. 'I suppose you've guessed by now that he happens to be a pretty important person around here!'

The pride that tinged her voice told Lee how highly Drew rated in his mother's scheme of things. How little she *really* knew of her son! 'Just call me Jean,' she said with a smile, 'everyone else does. I——' She broke off and Lee followed her gaze to a rather severe-looking woman of middle age who was standing in the doorway. 'Come in, Mrs Mac!' And to Lee: 'Meet our housekeeper, Mrs MacIntosh. She's the one who keeps the whole place going. I don't know how we'd get along without her, especially times when I have to rush off to judge events at a gymkhana or attend some countrywomen's get-together in another part of the country.'

The tightly-set lips parted in a smile. 'It's all part of my job,' the tall angular woman said primly, 'and so long as Drew is satisfied with me.' Lee could see how gratified the housekeeper was by the words of appreciation. This whole household, she mused, seemed to revolve around Drew. Look at the warm welcome given him by the other two women in the house. Well, she had no intention of joining the club, that was for sure.

When she had showered away the dust of the roads, Lee changed into a thin cotton knit shirt and faded blue jeans. She might as well look like a working member of the staff, she decided, seeing that was to be her status here.

She ran lightly down the stairs, to pause at the door of the dining room, now echoing with male voices. Then nerving herself to face a battery of curious eyes, she went into the room and was immediately conscious of a group of deeply-tanned, casually dressed men, glasses in their hands, who were gathered around Drew at the cocktail cabinet. No one appeared to have noticed Lee, so she stood by the doorway, trying to focus her attention on a sweep of lawn, flower-bordered, that she glimpsed through the french doors opening on to a side verandah. With another part of her mind, however, she was taking in the conversation echoing around her as Drew's staff plied him with questions in connection with his recent overseas trip to the U.K.

'Sorry, Lee,' Jean Hamilton hurried to her side, 'I meant to bring you along to the dining room, but I was delayed.' The men were moving towards the long table. 'You sit by me, Katrina——' but the other girl who had come into the room with Mrs Hamilton had already dropped down beside Drew at the head of the table.

'Hi!' said a voice close to Lee's ear, and she glanced up to see a boyish face. She took in a wide and cheerful grin, a sprouting moustache, a thatch of thick brown hair.

'Oh, it's you, David!' Jean Hamilton turned to Lee with a smile. 'This is my younger son.'

'I heard on the grapevine that Drew had brought you back with him from Samoa,' said David. 'Quite a feat, getting around old Drew, I'd say—how'd you manage it?'

Lee found herself warming to this pleasant young man with the relaxed and friendly manner. Or could it be, the thought shot through her mind, that right at this moment any male who regarded her as just an ordinary girl instead of a scheming, mercenary type, was a welcome change? Aloud she answered smilingly, 'Put it down to that old island magic.'

Immediately the words left her lips she regretted them, for they gave an entirely false impression, she realised suddenly, of a romantic interlude amid flickering palm-trees and sandy beaches. She added quickly, 'Actually Drew's going to find me some work here.' Had she said the wrong thing again? she wondered, for both Jean Hamilton and David were looking—there was no other word for their expression—astounded.

Mrs Hamilton was the first to recover herself. 'That's nice,' she said lamely.

David said in his lighthearted way, 'Sounds like Drew. Keep 'em working, that's his motto. You'll get used to him after a while,' he confided to Lee, 'so just in case you might have got the wrong idea of him, seeing him lolling back in a deckchair in the sun over in Samoa, at home he's a tiger for work, you'll see——'

'Never mind about all that!' Katrina's high sweet tones cut across the masculine accents. 'Tell me, Drew, what did you bring back from the island? Anything interesting?'

How about me? Lee was tempted to say the words aloud, but at that moment she met Drew's sardonic glance and knew that the same thought had occurred to him.

'Come on,' pleaded Katrina, 'tell me what you've got for me. I did put in an order for one of those dreamy island frocks, all hand-printed with hibiscus flowers and so on, remember?'

Drew answered her in the tone of one placating a demanding child. 'You've got it.'

'And while we're on the subject of gifts,' David called from across the table, 'how about the cassette recorder you promised to get for me?'

'Your chances are fairly good in that direction.'

'And the special tapes?'

Laughing—he looked quite different when he laughed, Lee found herself thinking—Drew held up a protesting hand. 'Hand-out time is right after dinner,' he promised.

'Did you see Beverley while you were in Samoa?' his mother was asking. 'You haven't told me a word about her yet. Was she well? Did she send any messages for me?'

'She's fine,' Drew said in his laconic way, 'said to tell you she'll be home for Christmas!'

Jean appealed to Lee, hands thrown upwards in a

gesture of helplessness. 'You see what I have to contend with? I ask you! I practically had to nag him into breaking his trip home at Samoa to see his sister and that's all the news I can get out of him. Did you happen to meet Beverley when you were on the island, Lee?'

'Only for a short while. She gave us a lift out to the airport in her car.' Lee searched her mind for something to say and at last came up with, 'She seemed to be very happy.'

'Oh, that doesn't mean a thing,' Jean told Lee. 'Bev would be happy anywhere, especially in some odd part of the world. She's always on the go, travelling around. Just now she's working at the British Consulate office in Samoa, but I wouldn't be a bit surprised to hear any day that she's moved on to Canada or America or England.'

'I doubt it,' Drew drawled, 'she seemed pretty wrapped up in a boy-friend over there.'

'Now that's what I wanted to hear!' Jean turned to Lee. 'You can see how hard I have to work to find out anything I want to know.'

'She's only my sister,' Drew objected mildly. The next minute he became involved in a barrage of questions that were being fired at him around the table. The talk became general, sheep-station jargon that to Lee was almost as difficult to understand as a foreign language. She gathered that in the absence of the boss the head shepherd, Jim Brady, a solidly-built, serious-eyed young man with a quiet way of speaking, had been in charge of the work on the station. Two of the mares in the hill paddocks had foaled, he reported to Drew, and a seeing-eye dog had had to have the vet's attention. Lee sat silent as the tide of talk flowed around her. 'The shearers are due in the morning, that is if the weather holds.' Jim squinted towards the bright sunshine outside the window. 'We've got the yards full, so there shouldn't be any hold-ups. I was on the blower with the shearers this morning and they're all set to go ahead first thing tomorrow.'

'Good. How about the pump?' Drew enquired. 'Has it been okay lately? You'd better send someone up to the bush block, Jim, to round up stray cattle.'

'Can do.'

Every moment strengthened Lee's realisation that Drew was the owner-manager of a vast sheep and cattle station a long way from civilisation, with all the responsibilities that such a position entailed. It all made him seem to her more than ever remote from ordinary people like herself.

'I'm Ernie,' a voice broke across her musing, and she turned to the softly-spoken middle-aged man at her side. 'Book-keeper, tractor driver, possum shooter, you name it. I sleep out in a bach down by the stables, but I take the odd meal with Drew and his family, especially,' his eyes twinkled in a tanned lined face, 'when it's a special occasion, like Drew coming home after a trip. Having a holiday here, are you?'

She smiled across at the genial face. 'In a way. Drew brought me over with him from Samoa for a visit.' Before she could encounter the unspoken query in his eyes for some reason she couldn't understand, the idea of Drew bringing a strange girl back with him from an overseas visit was simply unbelievable to everyone here—she trotted out her explanation. 'I'm going to work for him.'

His silence lasted only a moment. 'Is that so?'

Why shouldn't she work here, for heaven's sake, everyone else did! That was, all except Katrina, and she was one of the family—and decorative as well. Drew would never expect Katrina to work on the station.

The food, Lee thought, was excellent with its cold meats and varieties of salads, freshly-baked bread and a choice of chutneys and sauces. There was no doubt, she mused, that the housekeeper looked after the family well.

When the meal came to an end, her hostess threw Lee an apologetic glance. 'I have to ride over to see a sick neighbour today and I'll be away for ages. You've no idea how distant a neighbour can be in this part of the world, but Katrina will take care of you.'

Lee felt relieved that Jean Hamilton wasn't forced to put herself out on Lee's account. For however Drew's family might regard her stay at the homestead, she knew she was no ordinary guest *and Drew knew it too*. She wrenched her mind back to the pleasant tones. 'Katrina,' Mrs Hamilton appealed to the girl seated further along the table, 'will you show Lee around the place this afternoon? Maybe she'd like to go for a ride.'

To Lee the silence seemed to last for ever. Clearly, she mused, the suggestion didn't appeal to the other girl one little bit. At last Katrina answered, her voice tinged with contempt. '*Can* you ride, Lee?'

'No.' a dimple flickered at the corner of Lee's mouth, 'but I've always wanted to learn?'

Help came from an unexpected quarter. 'That's the spirit!' Jim Brady told her encouragingly. 'You'll have a ton of fun, pick it up in no time at all!'

Later that afternoon as she went with a reluctant Katrina towards the stables, Lee wondered a trifle nervously if she were about to be provided with a flighty mount. As Katrina led from the stables a heavy, aged mare with a lacklustre eye, however, Lee knew her fears to be groundless. She watched as Katrina slipped a bridle on her head, tossed a blanket, followed by a saddle, on the broad back.

Lee reached up to pat the big head. 'What's his name?'

'It's not a he, it's a she—Gypsy.'

Lee bit back the angry retort that trembled on her lips. 'She looks quiet enough. I don't think I'll be in any danger of falling off on her.'

'Quiet! Gypsy's so quiet she's just about immobile,' said Katrina scathingly. She added with assumed carelessness, 'We keep one or two horses like Gypsy for any children who happen to be staying here. Very young children.'

'Really!' The annoying thing about the other girl's obvious dislike of herself was that Katrina happened to be on her home ground and Lee had no comeback.

'You'd better get up,' said Katrina. 'Not that side, stupid!'

Lee set her teeth together. She wouldn't give up her chance to learn to ride, no matter what Katrina said! Somehow she scrambled up on to the saddle, aware all the time of Katrina's contemptuous glance. It cost her quite an effort to ask, 'Are you coming with me?'

Katrina tossed her fair head. 'I've got more important things to do with my time, but you'll be all right if you don't try to break any speed records.' All at once her tone was friendly. 'Why don't you go up the hill track? You can see for miles up on the ridge.' She walked alongside horse and rider.

'Hill track?' Lee was getting accustomed to the plodding motion of her mount and the sensation of being so high in the air. 'There seem to be so many hills.'

'Any one will do. I'll show you.' Still with a hand on the bridle, Katrina led her through a shelterbelt of tall poplars and up a grassy rise. Ahead Lee could see a track winding up a grass-covered cliff. She would need to hang on with everything she had—knees, hands, heels, she thought in near panic, if she were to keep her seat on a slope that looked to be almost perpendicular. Pride, however, forbade her turning back, the malicious gleam in Katrina's brown eyes saw to that, so Lee turned Gypsy towards the track.

'On your way! It's all yours!' Katrina gave the mare a sharp flick with a switch she was carrying, then it seemed to Lee that everything was happening at once.

Like a suddenly released spring, Gypsy gave a gigantic leap upwards, taking the cliff track at speed. Instinctively Lee grabbed handfulls of the flowing mane and clung on tightly. Instinct too made her lean forward low in the saddle. That was all she could think of, hanging on at all costs, as sky and hill flew dizzily past. She didn't know how much longer the ordeal was going to continue, all that mattered was that she had to keep her balance, clinging tightly to the streaming mane, expecting at every moment to be tossed down the slope.

One last long bound of her mount and they were up on flat ground at the summit of the hill. Lee pulled on the reins and Gypsy stood still. The mare was breathing hard and perspiration streaked the black coat.

'That was a pretty good show you put on just now.' She straightened and, still breathless, realised the head shepherd was reining in his stock horse beside her. 'I thought,' he said, grinning, 'you'd never ridden a horse before?'

'I haven't, honestly.' Her eyes glimmered. Now that it was all over she found she could laugh about it. 'I was simply terrified! Gypsy looked so quiet and solid I didn't think she'd have it in her to go loping up the cliff like that!'

He sent her a meaningful look. 'She hasn't, not unless someone gives her a hefty swipe to start her on the way up.'

The thoughts crowded Lee's mind. Katrina, carrying a switch with her, suggesting that she should take the cliff track. The girl had meant her to have a fall, she realised now, and Jim Brady had witnessed the incident. She said slowly, 'Was that Katrina's idea of a joke, do you think?'

'Sure was. You're not the first new rider she's tried it out on. Mind you, if you'd baled out back there on the cliff it would have been a chance for me to do my big rescue act.' He grinned his friendly grin. 'Pity, I'd have enjoyed that.'

Lee laughed, her good humour restored. 'Stick around, you'll probably have lots of chances yet with me and Gypsy!'

'Rubbish! You've got the makings of a first class rider. Look what you did just now! Sticking on like glue going up that incline at speed takes some doing—anyway, now that you're here, how about a ride around to see a bit of the property?'

Lee hesitated. 'I'd like that—but aren't you working?'

'Work? What's that? It's my day off and I can't think of a better way to spend it than showing a guest around the place. The boss usually does that with visitors at the station. Half his luck!' He placed a hand on Gypsy's bridle. 'Not to worry, we'll stick to the flat ground up here. Even if we didn't, I'd take care of you.'

All at once she felt a sense of security in the company of this friendly shepherd, and security, she mused, was something she had been short of during the past few days. Why couldn't Drew be more like Jim Brady, she thought as the two mounts paced along the dried grass side by side, instead of cruel and unfeeling and generally impossible to deal with?

As her companion's glance scanned the sheep-dotted paddocks in the distance, Lee asked, 'What are you looking for?'

'Anything that's out of order. You never know when you might come across a sick sheep, a hole in a fence, a fallen tree. It pays to keep an eye open all the time.'

'I suppose so.' Lee's gaze went over cleared hills with their grazing black cattle and beyond to ranges covered in heavy bush. A road zigzagged steeply down through little gullies and wound into the scrubland.

Jim followed her gaze. 'It's all station land. Those far hills are the northern boundary.'

She exclaimed in wonderment, 'It's so big!'

'It's big country all right, but Drew's the man to handle it. Ask anyone and they'll tell you that any guy who gets his training at Mahia can be sure of a job in any sheep or cattle station in the country. Drew happens to be the right man in the right job. It's a family thing and has been ever since his grandfather bought land from the Maoris over a hundred years ago.' He grinned. 'Doesn't look as though Drew's going to carry on the tradition, though.'

'You mean,' Lee couldn't understand why she was so interested in the subject, 'you don't think he'll ever marry?'

'Doesn't look like it. Not that he's given himself much chance in that direction. He hasn't bothered much with girls ever since Elaine—that was tough luck.'

Lee forgot to try and look uninterested in Drew's affairs of the heart and asked eagerly, 'What happened?'

'He didn't tell you about her? Guess he wouldn't, still doing his best to put her out of his mind, I expect. It's three years now since it happened. She was killed in a car smash four days before the wedding, just like that, she died instantly. After that, he threw himself into his work, long hours working from daylight to dark, no holidays—this trip overseas is the first break he's given himself in years. Guess his mother was hoping he'd meet up with some nice girl while he was away,' his eyes were on Lee's freckled young face, 'someone who'd make him forget——'

'Don't look at me,' Lee protested, aware of the teasing look in Jim's eyes, 'I'm just his travelling companion. Coming here together was just a matter of convenience. It didn't mean a thing——' At Jim's expression of surprise she broke off in confusion. Was she protesting too quickly, too emphatically, giving herself away? But what was there to give away? Nothing at all. It was just the awkwardness of the situation that was making her flush, she told herself, and felt the colour in her cheeks deepen as she caught Jim's expressive wink.

'If you say so,' Jim said easily, and to her relief, he changed the subject. 'This is the air-strip,' he told her as they turned into a long swathe of clipped green grass, 'where the "supermen" operate from. The stuff's stored in the shed at the end of the runway. Aerial topdressing has taken a lot of the sheer slog from bringing in these hill properties. Drew will probably take you up there to see the pilot taking off next time the dust is due to be sprinkled around. Visitors from the city seem to get quite a kick out of seeing the planes taxiing along the runway and skimming low over the slopes.'

Strange, Lee reflected as they moved along in the clear bright sunshine, how everyone on the station believes I'm a welcome guest, everyone except Drew. Why *must* I keep thinking of him all the time?

'Here's Drew now,' Jim was saying, as a horseman cantered up a grassy slope towards them. 'He's been down in the northern block blasting out a new water-hole.'

Lee couldn't understand herself. She couldn't bear the man at any price, so why, she asked herself helplessly, did she feel this ridiculous leap of her pulses at the sight of him? Now that she was seeing the enemy in his own terrain she couldn't help a sneaky feeling of admiration, but that was merely because of the way he looked. Wearing a cool open-necked shirt, fawn shorts, serviceable work boots, with his dark hair blowing back from a bronzed forehead he looked what he was, a back-country station owner, lean, sinewy, tough, and in spite of his casual attire, very much the boss! You could tell that, the thought ran through Lee's mind, by the disapproving light in his eyes as he took in the two riders.

Jim, however, appeared to be oblivious of Drew's scowling glance. 'Lee's learning to ride,' he said easily, 'making a good job of it too! She started horse-riding the hard way, came flat-stick up the cliff path and didn't put on the brakes until she got to the top.'

She was aware of Drew's glance moving from her flushed face to Jim's goodhumoured grin.

'You didn't lose much time,' he remarked, and you could tell by the way he was looking at her, Lee thought, incensed, that his words had nothing to do with the matter of her learning to ride!

'See you.' He turned his restive mount and galloped away.

Jim stared after Drew, a puzzled expression clouding his eyes. 'Wonder what's biting him?'

Lee pretended she had no idea as to the cause of the boss's ill humour and to her relief Jim dropped the subject. Later he saw her back to the stables, then showed her how to remove the saddle and bridle and rub down her mount.

She was feeling stiff from the unaccustomed exercise when at last she returned to the house, to find Katrina leaning over the verandah rail.

'Enjoy your ride?' There was a taunting glint in the big brown eyes.

'It was super!' Lee returned with enthusiasm. 'I'm going to have another go tomorrow. I can't wait!' She felt a surge of triumph as Katrina's expression changed from contempt to one of blank astonishment.

CHAPTER FOUR

THAT evening as everyone gathered in the lounge room after dinner, Drew gave his family the gifts he had brought back from overseas—for his mother, an English tailored hunting jacket, a cassette recorder for David, 'And for you, kitten,' he handed Katrina a long white box from which she lifted a Polynesian-style dress printed in a design of scarlet hibiscus blossoms.

'Thanks, Drew, it's just what I wanted!' She hurried from the room to return a few minutes later, her long fair hair flowing loose around her shoulders and feet bare beneath the ankle-length skirt. 'Like it?' She twirled around. 'If only I had some romantic island music I'd dance for you.'

'No problem,' said Drew in his laconic way, and fishing in his pocket he tossed a cassette to his brother. 'Try this one.'

'Samoan melody coming up—I hope.' David fitted the cassette in place and the next moment the haunting strains of island guitars throbbed through the room. Laughingly, Katrina moved in the rhythmic movements of the Pacific islands, hips swaying and hands fluttering, the long skirt flowing around her feet.

It was a melody she had heard before, Lee realised, in tropical surroundings on the night she had first set eyes on Drew. 'I know what music that is,' she cried impulsively, 'it's a recording of the guitars played by the Samoans at Aggie Grey's, the night of the barbecue beside the pool!'

'That's right.' Drew made no further comment.

David, however, was looking at his brother in a

74

puzzled fashion. 'You taped this at the hotel in Samoa where you and Lee were staying? Guess it must have been a night you wanted to remember. Something special, hmm?'

'What gives you that idea?' The boss's deadpan expression gave nothing away.

'He's trying to put me off,' David complained. He turned, grinning, to Lee. 'I'll never get the truth out of him, but *you* can tell me. It was a big night, I bet, something special? I get the picture of palm trees dark against the sunset, flares burning all over the place, perfume from the frangipani, beautiful dusky maidens, the lot, and you and Drew dancing on the grass—there was dancing on the grass?'

'Oh yes.' If only she weren't so aware of Drew's thunderous expression!

'There you are!' David cried triumphantly over the lilting notes, as Katrina continued to dance. 'I knew it! You two together——'

'Not on your life!' Drew's cool tones cut like a knife across David's teasing accents. 'Actually, we were the ones who weren't dancing!'

'Weren't dancing——' Something of the warning glint in his brother's eye must have got through to David, Lee thought, for he broke off with a shrug. 'Take it easy, brother. I was only asking!'

At that moment the housekeeper entered the room, telling Drew he was wanted on the telephone.

He got to his feet. 'I'll take it in the office.' Half an hour later, he hadn't returned. It must surely be that maddening autocratic manner of his, Lee mused, that made everything so flat once he had left the room.

It was late when at last goodnights were said. Indeed, Lee was the last to leave the room. Moving a little stiffly after what she privately termed her epic ride, she was going along the hall when a door opened and she looked up to meet Drew's unsmiling face. He stood in the doorway. 'Oh, Lee, I want a word with you—come in, will you?'

Now what? She preceded him into a room that seemed, in that first quick glance, to be filled with a huge desk. The walls were covered with cliphooks and calendars and photographs of show-jumpers. Drew swept a pile of papers from a low stool and pushed it towards her. 'Take a seat.'

She sat down gingerly. Past experience had proved that the boss never wanted to see her for anything pleasant; on the contrary.

He shot her a look from under his eyelids.

'Feeling all right after your ride?'

'Fine,' she lied. At least he was interested enough to enquire, she thought, that was something.

'Good? Now about that job you wanted me to jack up for you——'

Oh, she might have known his interest in her health had nothing to do with her! How could she have fooled herself into thinking that he was at last being friendly? She did her best to hide the anger mushrooming up inside her and made her voice flat and disinterested. 'Oh, the job? Yes, of course. Has something come up?'

'Has it ever!' he rasped. 'I've been on the phone all evening, buzzing every contact I've got on the books, but I've drawn a blank every time. And that,' his level penetrating stare was disconcerting, 'leaves me with you!'

She shot him a startled blue glance. 'What do you mean?'

He tilted his swivel chair, leaning back to eye her consideringly. 'Cook for the shearing gang, how does that strike you?'

'*What?*'

'That's it! I've got a message tonight that the woman who was engaged to come tomorrow to cook for the shearers is ill. She won't be turning up in the morning, neither will anyone else, judging by the replies I've had to enquiries. So it's up to you!'

'Me?' Lee's voice was a horrified squeak. She stared at him incredulously. 'But I can't cook!'

It wasn't strictly true, of course. She had once worked for a short period of time at a private school, preparing lunches for staff and pupils, but one could scarcely put such work in the same category as coping with the requirements of a shearing gang with king-sized appetites.

Drew took not the slightest notice of her protest. 'You'll soon learn.' *The brute!*

'When would I get a chance to learn?' she demanded. 'Aren't the shearers coming tomorrow?'

'Five-thirty start!' He seemed to take a positive delight in telling her. He bent on her his deep compelling gaze. 'You do want to get back to England, don't you?'

Two spots of colour flamed in her cheeks. 'I can't think of anything better,' she flung at him, 'than getting away from here!'

'Well then, here's your chance. You wanted a job, I'm handing it to you. Now get on with it!'

At that moment, it seemed to Lee, something rose in her, determination, pride—whatever it was made her face him bravely. *Think of it as a challenge, girl.* Could that be her own voice saying clearly, decisively, 'All right then, I'll give it a go!'

'Good girl! There's nothing to it!'

Nothing to it. Just what, she wondered in horror, had she let herself in for?

'Look,' he was saying, 'I'd better put you in the picture. It's a matter of split-second timing, of course.

The men work a long day, six to six, and they'll be here for the best part of a week.' He got to his feet. 'You'd better come with me and I'll show you over the place so you can get an idea of where you'll be working in the morning.'

The morning! Lee was making a mental calculation. She would need to get up at four! Luckily she had her little travel alarm clock with her.

Feeling as though she were in the toils of some dreadful nightmare, she went with him. Outside the stars were brilliant in the dark dome overhead. It was very still, the only sound the piping of cicadas. They passed through a small gate and she climbed into a waiting Land Rover. When they reached the dim bulk of the woolshed, the darkness seemed impenetrable and Drew put out a hand to help her up the high steps leading up to the wide doors above. Suddenly she felt a thrill of fire shoot through her. He had to hold her tightly, it was nothing to him. Yet the wild excitement still pulsed through her.

Then he released her to fling open the big doors. He switched on lights and immediately the high-raftered shed leaped into sight—the presses, floors shiny with the grease of fleeces, the shute, wool bales. But Lee had little time to notice it all, as Drew was striding through a door at the rear. Once again he put a hand to a light switch. 'This is the kitchen where you'll work. There's swags of room, stacks of provisions, all the latest equipment.'

She gazed around the spacious room with its massive refrigerator and long table in the centre. Her gaze went to a gleaming white electric range and above it, racks of outsized pots and pans. How could she ever manage to lift the great cumbersome things?

'The power's switched on and you'll find meat ready cut up in the fridge.' He swung open the door, revealing enormous piles of mutton. 'For breakfast they'll have fried chops. That's after porridge, of course.'

'P-porridge?' she said faintly, wondering once again what she had let herself in for.

'Toasters are in here,' he swung open a cupboard, 'and this one,' he swung open another cupboard door, 'has jam, honey, marmalade. Tea's the main thing.' Lee gasped as he pointed to massive aluminium teapots. 'Well, that disposes of breakfast.'

If only it did, she thought despairingly. How could she ever cope with all this?

'Main thing to remember,' Drew was saying, 'is that that's on the table by five-thirty. The gang get paid by the bale and they don't believe in wasting time.' He added carelessly, 'You could shove a couple of roasts in the oven after breakfast is done with. You could have one cold for lunch, with salads, of course. You'll find all the makings in the fridge. Smoko's at ten o'clock. You could rattle up some scones and sandwiches for that.'

Just like that! The way he was speaking, Lee thought crossly, anyone would think all this food prepared itself.

'Afternoon smoko's at three sharp,' he was saying. 'Scones and sandwiches do for that too.'

Didn't the shearing gang ever stop eating? Lee wondered wildly.

'Dinner won't worry you too much.' *That's what you think!* 'A big pot of stew or a pan of roast mutton and vegetables always goes down well. They're not fussy about variety, mutton does them every time.'

Her sense of inadequacy was growing with each passing moment, but something even stronger urged her on. She wouldn't allow him to intimidate her! She would just have to do her best and hope for a miracle.

'Oh, about smokos, you shove teapots and eats into a box,' he hauled a wooden crate down from a shelf, 'the men plug in the electric jug in the shed and make the tea there. Get one of them to give you a hand to carry it out. That's about it. You'll be through fairly early. The gang are usually in bed by seven ready for an early start in the morning. If you've got any spare time through the day——'

'Spare time!' Lee could remain silent no longer. 'You must be joking!' Drew didn't even smile.

They went back through the long shed and Lee waited outside on the landing when he switched off the lights and closed the heavy doors. After the lighted shed she couldn't see a yard in front of her and would have plunged down into nothingness had he not caught her in his arms and pulled her upwards. 'It's tricky in the dark. Thisaway, the steps are a long way apart, now.' An arm firmly around her shoulders, he guided her down the steps. It was a perfectly normal thing for him to do, she told herself as he released her on the short dried grass below, so why was she trembling? Not fear of the boss, and it couldn't be love— how absurd could you get? It must, she decided, be a physical thing, for even hating him as she did, she had to admit that he projected a male aura that was little short of devastating. With an effort she tried to concentrate on what he was telling her. Not that she wanted to hear the details of that appalling job that loomed ahead of her in four hours' time—four hours, she thought in desperation.

'Have you an alarm clock?'

'Oh yes.' The clock, she thought, was the least of her problems.

That night she dreamed of Drew, Drew with an unaccustomed tenderness in his eyes, believing in her, loving—— The image was shattered by a thunderous tattoo on her door and the sight of the man himself as he thrust a dark head around the door. 'Lee! Are you awake?'

She sat up abruptly, shaking the short curly hair back from her eyes in an effort to separate the dream from the unpleasant reality. For Drew's face expressed anything but tenderness, he looked definitely impatient, and disapproving of her, as usual.

'Time to get up!'

Realisation came with a rush! 'Help!' She gave an anguished glance towards the small gold travel clock that had let her down when she most needed it.

'Pick you up in ten minutes!' he said, and vanished.

Never in her life had Lee dressed so swiftly, pulling on underwear, snatching up a cotton top, getting into jeans and thrusting her feet into rubber thongs. In the bathroom she splashed her face with cold water, ran a comb through her hair and was ready in seven minutes flat, which was pretty good going, she thought.

Evidently Drew didn't think so. He was waiting in the Land Rover as she hurried out of the back door. A brief 'Hop in' and they were moving down the driveway.

'I could easily have walked, you know,' she said as they took the track winding towards the woolshed.

'Quicker this way.'

'I suppose. How many men are there in the shearing gang,' she enquired, 'three, four?'

'A dozen, actually.'

'Oh!' She was still mentally engaged working out quantities of oatmeal, cups of water and how many chops each man would eat—she fancied shearers would have massive appetites—when Drew pulled up at the wool shed.

'Good luck!' he called, as she dropped to the dew-wet grass and you could tell by the sardonic look in his eyes, she thought, that he expected her to make a mess of it. But she would show him, she vowed, she'd prove to him she could meet his challenge, even if it killed her!

In the big kitchen leading off the shearing shed, Lee frantically turned on switches on the electric stove. Porridge first ... She thrust a cup deep into an immense bag of rolled oats. There were no directions on the packet and Lee pondered over the required quantities. One cup of oats to three cups of water should do it, but should the water be hot or cold? She took a chance on hot, it was quicker that way, then found she couldn't get rid of the lumps. At last she threw out the mixture and set a fresh lot of porridge bubbling on the stove. Now for the chops. Lifting down the heavy pans from a shelf, she threw in dripping and added the mutton. A swift calculation and she came up with three hefty mutton chops per man. Ready-cut loaves of bread were a gift from heaven and so too was the electric pop-up toaster. With luck she would manage breakfast without too much trauma.

Ten minutes later, though, as she stirred porridge that had somehow turned into hard lumps, her hopes fell flat. It would have to do, she thought desperately, there was no time for a third attempt. She turned her attention to the meat which for some strange reason wasn't cooking at all. Help! She had switched on an oven element by mistake. Frantically she turned the switch to 'high'. In her haste and confusion it seemed only a few minutes later when as she was pouring boiling water into an enormous enamel teapot, the shearing gang came crowding in at the door.

'Morning, miss.' A massive Maori man paused beside her, a cheerful smile lighting his face. 'Breakfast on yet?'

She pushed the curly hair back from her flushed

forehead. 'Just waiting for you,' she said with more confidence than she felt, and began ladling out lumpy porridge into plates.

'G'day, miss! G'day! Good morning!' With friendly grins the gang took their places at the table, tough-looking men with skins burned to the colour of mahogany and powerful muscles rippling beneath their black sweat shirts.

The porridge went down without complaints, Lee noticed apprehensively. Maybe the gang were in too much of a hurry to get on with their work to worry about it. At that moment, alerted by a strong smell of burning, she rushed from toaster to stove, where the mutton was singed black and a flame shot high from fat dropped on to the element. Before she could move the hot pan aside, a masculine hand came to her rescue and she turned to face a slight, fair-haired young man with a friendly grin. 'Anyone for flambéed mutton this morning?' he asked the gang, and was answered by deep guffaws of laughter.

How could they laugh? Lee wondered desperately, aware of the meat that was raw inside and burned to cinders on the outside. It seemed, however, that the shearing gang were a tough breed and took such incidents in their stride, for in no time at all the plates were emptied. At least, Lee thought in near-panic, she couldn't go wrong with a pop-up toaster and tea, tea, tea. Never had she seen men drink tea in such vast quantities.

When the meal was over the gang wasted no time. Stubbing out cigarettes, they pushed their chairs back from the table and filed out. The room was suddenly quiet as they left the kitchen and trooped into the shed to begin their day's work.

Their day's work! Lee looked at the mounds of dirty dishes. And to think she was expected to produce more food for—what did they call their morning tea break, smoko?—in just a few hours' time. One thing, she comforted herself, she was confident of success when it came to whipping up a batch of scones. It wasn't until later, as she took a tray of hard, bullet-like objects from the oven, that she remembered she had neglected to add baking powder to the mixture.

She sent a frenzied glance towards the clock on the bench, then bit her lip. Even the shearers wouldn't eat those rock-like offerings, she thought helplessly, and looked up to meet Drew's lopsided grin. He was standing in the doorway, thumbs hooked in his hip belt, taking it all in, and he was looking—*amused*!

'It's all very well for you to laugh!' Lee was past caring what she said. 'Look at that, will you! And that!' She tossed the stone-like objects down on the bench. Tears of rage and mortification glittered in her eyes and she blinked them away. 'And don't start telling me to get going and make another batch, because there just isn't time! I hate that clock!' she added viciously.

He cocked thick black eyebrows. 'You're not doing very well with the baking, are you?'

Lee all but choked with anger. 'You—you——'

'Not that it matters all that much,' he observed carelessly.

She stared up at him wrathfully. 'What do you mean?'

'Can't you guess?' His crooked smile was definitely not of the heartwarming variety. 'You didn't make enough to feed even a couple of those guys!'

Lee found her voice at last. 'They were meant to be twice that size!' she spluttered. 'They would have been too, if I hadn't forgotten to put in the rising.'

He shrugged broad shoulders. 'Still wouldn't have gone anywhere with the gang you've got to feed.'

'All right, then!' She was feeling too frustrated to argue the matter further. 'So I didn't make enough— but what,' she wailed, 'am I going to do about smoko?'

'No problem.' He seemed scarcely interested in her troubles. 'You'll have to double up on sandwiches, that's all. How about the mutton? Did you shove a couple of roasts in the oven?'

'Of course I did. Well, one anyway. Heavens! I'd better check——' She flew to open the oven door, to be met by a cloud of smoke. In a second Drew was at her side, turning the switches to 'low' and closing the oven door.

'You'll get used to it all in a day or two,' he drawled.

Lee doubted it. '*If* I last that long!' she threw at him.

He ignored that. 'That'll take care of lunch. You can shove another roast in the oven for the night's meal.'

Her brain was whirling. 'But what about smoko? I'll have to give them something on the bread.'

'Salmon's your best bet,' he advised unfeelingly. 'Stick a few lettuce leaves with it and you'll be away, laughing.'

He was full of suggestions, she thought hotly. Why couldn't he help her instead of standing there doling out advice in that superior manner of his that he must know only made her feel more frustrated than ever.

'Hi, Drew!' Katrina had come into the kitchen. She looked, Lee thought resentfully, dewy cool and utterly carefree, her smooth blonde hair freshly washed and shining. No wonder Drew's gaze softened as he looked at her.

At last the other girl's glance moved to Lee. 'Hello! You look as though you've been working.'

'I am working!' Lee's soft lips were set in a firm line. All at once she was unhappily aware of beads of per- spiration on her forehead, her hair tousled into disorder where she had run her fingers through it in frustration during the last two hours, smears of grease on her T-shirt that had been snowy-white earlier on.

Katrina laughed, high and childlike. 'Did you hear that, Drew? She wants to get rid of us! Don't worry, Lee, I won't hold you up. I only popped in to bring you these.' She set down a cardboard carton on the table. 'Jean said to tell you she's got oodles of corn fritters in the deep freeze. She thought they might help out.'

Lee lifted a corner of the white napkin to see piles of fritters, golden, appetising and *ready cooked*! Would they ever!

'Jean said to tell you to heat them up in the pan if you want to prepare them for smoko this morning.' The other girl's voice lacked the usual note of condescension when speaking to Lee but Lee was too strung-up to notice. 'They're not all that wonderful,' Katrina added, for Lee was eyeing the carton as if it were filled with precious jewels.

'They are to me! Tell Jean I'll thank her when I get back to the house tonight.'

'Okay, kitten,' Drew laid a hand on Katrina's rounded arm, 'Lee's got work to do!' Lee could hear them laughing together as they moved out into the shearing shed. Somehow she no longer cared about Katrina. Life had narrowed down to mundane matters like electric stoves and sandwiches. Reaching up to a shelf, she began opening tins of salmon in such haste that she cut her hand and had to waste precious moments finding the First Aid box and applying a Band-aid.

Promptly at ten o'clock Lee transferred piles of sandwiches and corn fritters to a wooden crate, adding two massive teapots, tea, sugar, milk and mugs. Then picking up the box she staggered towards the shearing

shed. The hot air rushed at her as she opened the door
to a scene of ceaseless activity. Shearers stripped to the
waist, perspiration running down their tanned muscular chests, bent low as they sheared away the thick
creamy wool from the sheep. Picking her way past
heaps of fleeces lying on the floor, she put the box
down on a bench and conscious of the smell of the
fleeces, glanced around the high-rafted shed.

One of the gang was tossing fleeces into a press and
another was tramping them down tight. At that
moment a cry of 'Sheepo' echoed through the shearing
shed and a rouseabout hurried to fill up the shearers'
catching pen. A Maori member of the gang who had
greeted her, could it have been only this morning? was
wielding a long broom as he swept up a litter of wool
pieces on the oil-slippery floor.

Her glance moved to a pile of filled bales and she
noticed that the fair-haired young man who had come
to her rescue at breakfast time was busy sewing up the
bales and marking each one with a black stencil,
'MAHIA'. It was all a strange unknown world to her,
the oppressive heat, the noise of the machines, the
fleeces piled high on the floor.

At that moment the machines were switched off and
in the sudden silence the men wiped their sweating
necks and shoulders and chests with towels hanging on
the door, then they dropped down to seat themselves
on the wool-filled bales. Someone switched on the
electric jug and tea was quickly made and brewed.
Mug after mug was emptied and filled again as thirsty
men gulped down the hot liquid. Lee was kept busy
pouring out while at her side the fair-haired young
man handled a second teapot.

She flashed him a grateful smile. 'You'd better pour
one for yourself. At the rate you're going you'll never
get around to it.'

'Not to worry. I can do that too.' His speech, Lee noticed, had a slightly different inflection from the rest of the gang, but there was no time for further conversation. Already the shearers were on their feet, and moving back towards stands and presses. Soon the shed once again bustled with activity.

Back in the kitchen—how she hated that kitchen!— Lee set to work feverishly washing piles of breakfast plates and smoko mugs. Somehow she got the dishes out of the way. Never had she known time to pass so swiftly. As lunch time approached she found that one of the mutton roasts appeared to be cooked. She took it out of the oven to cool, put potatoes on to boil and began preparing plates of bread and butter. Would she or wouldn't she, she wondered frantically, have the meal ready in time? She did, but only by a minute or so. Despite their hours of exhausting toil, the gang came in from the washroom happy and relaxed and, she thought despairingly, no doubt as ravenous as ever. A few moments later, though, she had reason to be thankful for their voracious appetites, for the roast was barely cooked and again they ate the unappetising food uncomplainingly. 'Meat's rare today,' one of the gang remarked. 'Anyone prefer their rations that way? Doesn't matter anyway, that's what you're going to get!'

'I'll put it back in the oven for a bit later on,' Lee suggested hopefully.

'You'd be so lucky!' Huge grins spread over deeply tanned masculine faces. And indeed, cooked or not, the meat vanished, together with the potatoes and the huge mounds of bread and butter. Lee wondered faintly whether her disastrous attempts at scones would have gone down too, had she put them on the table.

Smoko at three o'clock! How could the hours since lunch have fled by? Afterwards she cooked rice in a pot to save time, then strained the cereal and poured over milk, adding sugar and transferring it all to a massive pie-dish that went into the oven. She peeled a mountain of potatoes and sliced mounds of cabbage. The meal was ready when the gang, freshly showered, filed in at the door and seated themselves at the table. By some miracle the meat was succulent and well cooked, but now Lee was too tired to care. When the meal, washed down with mugs of tea, was over, the men wished her goodnight and went to their quarters. The lanky young man with the friendly smile, however, didn't follow the others. Lee had dropped to a chair, feeling too exhausted at the moment to begin washing the mountain of mutton-smeared plates, when she looked up to meet his considerate gaze.

'You look all in. This is all new to you, isn't it?'

She tossed the damp hair back from her forehead and summoned a smile. 'Does it show so much? Don't tell me! It was that awful half-cooked roast at lunch time that gave me away!'

'It wasn't so bad. I've eaten a lot worse fare than that on the shearing circuit.' He straddled a chair and grinned at her over the littered table. 'Shall I tell you something? Life in the shed is all fairly new to me too.'

Lee was feeling so weary that the room seemed to be moving around her in waves of tiredness. The masculine tones seemed to reach her as from a distance. 'I come from a sheep station too, not half so big as Mahia, but it's still fairly extensive. It's a few hours away from here as the crow flies, or the Land Rover goes. I've been away from home a lot, missed out on getting the know-how of station life. This is the best way I know of getting experience.'

She gave him a glimmer of a smile. 'You're doing it the hard way, like me.'

'That's right, Lee—don't look so surprised, I soon

found out your name. Mine's Paul—Paul Forrest. That accounts for me, but you——' She fancied there was compassion in his tone. His frankly appreciative gaze took in her wan young face, her small soft hands that were criss-crossed with strips of plaster covering burn marks and cuts. 'What is it with you? Are you planning to write articles and getting the shearing shed gen at first hand? Getting experience?'

'You could call it that. I can tell you this much, though,' she said with conviction, 'for me this is a oncer. I'll make money some other way, cleaning, dish-washing, cooking, but not all together, with one eye kept on the clock?'

'I don't blame you!' He had a singularly sweet smile, she thought. 'You may have heard of my dad's sheep station, White Range?'

She shook her head. 'I'm a newcomer to this country. I've just come out from England. I wanted a job so——'

He stared at her incredulously. 'And you took on this!'

'Well, it's a job.' Not for anything would she reveal the fact that she had been forced into working for Drew Hamilton. He had known what she was in for, yet he had left her no option. How could he? But of course he was an expert when it came to retaliation. Just thinking of him made her feel angry all over again. She would never forgive him for letting her in for this—never!

The pleasant masculine tones intruded on her vindictive imaginings. What was he saying? Something about dishes?

'We'll lick these into shape in no time!' He got to his feet and began to gather together plates and mugs.

'No!' She shook her head and the curly hair flew from side to side. 'I'll do them.' She stretched her arms. 'I've got all night and until five-thirty in the morning. I wouldn't think of letting you in for the job.'

'The way I see it,' he was at the sink stacking plates, 'you haven't got any choice.'

'What about your twelve-hour stint tomorrow?'

'What about yours?'

Weakly, Lee gave in. Indeed no one, she thought, watching him at the sink bench as he tossed wet plates on the drainer, would believe he had worked through such a hard day. He must be tougher than he looked. When the job was done, greasy oven pans and all, he wiped down the long table and hung the washcloth up to dry. 'Told you it wouldn't take long. I'll be on my way now.' He paused in the doorway. 'Coming?'

'No,' Lee smiled up into the friendly face, 'I'll just do a few things first, get ahead of myself a bit. You know?'

'Okay. See you in the morning.'

He was nice, she thought, as the sound of his footsteps faded. His help and thoughtfulness had been the one bright spot in an exhausting day. Immediately she forgot him. If she could prepare the porridge in advance tonight she would need only to warm it up in the morning. Burned porridge and blackened chops! She felt a wild urge towards hysteria. It was all Drew's fault. He had forced her into doing the work in spite of her inexperience, merely because it suited his plans to employ her, because he couldn't find anyone else. Yet in spite of heat and exhaustion. she wasn't going to admit failure—not yet!

Once she began work again she found endless tasks demanding her attention, for this was her chance to get a head start in the morning. She looked at the long freezer. Why not make scones tonight? The shearers didn't need to have them freshly made. Indeed, she mused wryly, the way in which she was managing things, they would be lucky to have them at all! She worked on, forcing herself to concentrate on the matter in hand despite the waves of tiredness that washed over her at intervals.

Much later she caught the sound of heavy footfalls in the shearing shed. Probably, she thought, one of the men had called in to collect his gear. Or perhaps David was coming in search of her, wondering why she hadn't appeared at the dinner table this evening. She was standing at the sink bench, washing a baking tray, when she glanced back over her shoulder to meet Drew's enigmatical gaze.

'Still at it?' To her distraught mind he seemed to be mocking her, pointing out how slow and inept she was at the task. Was that what he was thinking?

'Just clearing up a few things,' she said airily, and went on wiping down the aluminium tray.

'At eleven o'clock at night?'

That really startled her into awareness. 'It can't be!'

'See for yourself.' She followed his glance towards the Big Ben ticking away over the sink.

'I'm just about through,' she said huffily. Her tone of voice said: And I don't need you around to oversee things.

He perched himself on the edge of the table, swinging a tanned leg and regarding her with his sardonic glance. 'Better call it a day,' he advised, 'or else——'

'I won't be fit to cope in the morning. I suppose that's what you mean!' She flung down the tray with a rattle.

'No shearing without the cook,' he agreed smoothly.

Suddenly the anger mushrooming up inside her exploded in a black cloud. 'You don't care about me! You don't care about *anything* so long as your shearing gets done on time!'

'You agreed to take it on,' he reminded her relentlessly.

'After you'd pushed me into it!' she flashed back.

'You could put it that way.'

It wasn't so much the words as the flicker of triumphant satisfaction in his eyes that infuriated her. A suspicion shot into her mind and the resentment inside her spilled over.

'It was all a put-up job to punish me for something I didn't even do!' Her blue eyes blazed up at him. 'I bet that cook you spoke to on the phone isn't really ill at all. I bet you told her not to come! You knew you could talk me into taking on the job because—because of what happened in Samoa. All the time——' she broke off, appalled at his expression. His eyes glittered dangerously and a muscle twitched in his cheek.

'Never question my word again! Understand?' His voice held a savage rasp and she took a step backwards, half expecting him to shake an apology from her.

'All right, all right, I believe you!' Strangely enough, it was the truth. Ruthless and authoritative though she knew him to be, deep down something told her that he wouldn't lie or cheat.

'So long as we've got that sorted out.' A little of the anger had lifted from his expression. 'Come on,' he went on in a low constrained tone, 'you'd better catch up with some sleep. I'll see you back to the house.'

'If you like.' All at once she was feeling desperately weary, but even through the tiredness sweeping over her she was aware of his glance. Why was he gazing at her in that penetrating way? The answer came the next minute.

'It's as hot as Hades in the shed when the presses are in full swing. You'd better wear some light gear tomorrow,' he told her curtly, 'shorts, a swimsuit, anything that lets in the air.'

Lee was only too aware of the discomfort en-
gendered by close-fitting denim jeans and heavy
cotton knit T-shirt. She had however, had just about
enough for one night of commands from this man. She
lifted her small chin high. 'I'll wear what I like!'

'Please yourself.' He switched off lights and they
went through the big empty shed together. On the
landing Drew closed the shed door and Lee stood
blinking in the intense darkness that she had never
before encountered. Always in the past there had been
city lights, or the reflected glow of a city's street lamps,
but this moonless night held a blackness one could
almost touch. All the same, she remembered the high
steps from the landing; if he imagined she didn't know
her way he was mistaken. 'I don't need——' It was
useless to protest, for he had an arm firmly around
her, and Lee tried to make herself stiff and un-
responsive to his touch. Indeed, she was concentrating
so much on the closeness of the enemy, as she privately termed him, that once again she missed her foot-
ing on a step and for a dizzy moment she found herself
caught close to his sinewy chest. She essayed a nerv-
ous laugh. Mustn't let anything happen to the cook!

She was still acutely aware of his closeness as he
took her down the high steps. Too much so for her
own peace of mind. For somehow she was finding it
difficult to hate the boss with this wild excitement
sending her thoughts flying wildly, so that nothing
mattered but his exciting, traitorous nearness. What
could be the matter with her to let Drew—Drew of all
men—affect her this way? Put it down to over-tired-
ness, she told herself later that night, a moment before
sleep claimed her.

CHAPTER FIVE

To Lee, the next few days slipped by in a frenzy of long hours and gruelling toil and she lost count of everything else in the world but the task of the moment and the seemingly endless preparation of vast quantities of food. After the first nightmare day she rallied herself, feeling more comfortable wearing a sleeveless cotton shift with a low scooped neckline. True, the clock was still her enemy against whom she fought a constantly losing battle but at least she felt a little more in charge of the situation. Paul helped. Each night when dinner was over he threw foaming detergent into hot water in the sink and cheerfully attacked a mountain of greasy plates. 'You're in training as a dish-washer instead of a shearer!' Lee told him laughingly. That was one of the nights when she could still laugh in spite of the weariness that now seemed to be a part of her life.

It was the longest and most exhausting week that Lee had ever known, but at last it came to an end. The last remnants of fleece were swept from the slippery floor and wool bales, sewn and marked with a black stencilled name MAHIA, were piled in stacks awaiting the trucks that would take them to a depot.

That night at dinner the men were relaxed and in high spirits as jokes and good natured chaffing echoed around the table. Afterwards they bade her goodbye, each man in turn taking her small hand in a powerful grip.

'It's been nice knowing you Lee.'

'Hope we meet up again before long.'

She laughed ruefully as she looked up at a burly shearer. 'You couldn't mean that, not after the ghastly blunders I made with the meals!' But they really did mean what they said, she realised in some surprise. 'Golly,' she told them, 'you must have had some pretty terrible messes served up to you then!'

'You wouldn't believe it! Remember that stint down south——' They proceeded to outdo one another in recounting meals of such horrific content that Lee didn't know whether or not to believe them.

Paul was the last to leave, his hand holding hers in a lingering grip.

'Thanks for everything,' she said with a smile. 'Goodness knows how ever I'd have got through all that dish-washing without your help!'

'A pleasure, and I mean that!' His warm gaze lingered on her face. 'I'll be seeing you again? If it wasn't that I was stuck with this shearing job on the next station for all of next week,' his low tone was tinged with regret, 'but after that? I could ring you and arrange something? You'll still be here?'

Lee had been trying to work out the amount of money due to her from her stint in the shed. High pay it might be but it wouldn't be sufficient to let her off the hook with Drew Hamilton. No such luck! Aloud she murmured on a sigh, 'Oh yes, I'll still be here,' and told herself silently, I might just as well be a prisoner.

'Tremendous!' Paul's young face had lighted up. 'I'll phone you next week. Until then——' he leaned down to plant a kiss on her mouth and before she could say anything further, he had turned abruptly and was moving towards the door. 'See you!' He flung a grin over his shoulder, his face flooded with such sudden happiness that Lee suspected he hadn't had many girl-friends in the past. The next moment she forgot him.

Strange to think how much at home she felt in this kitchen, she thought as she ran a damp mop over the linoleum covered floor. The electric range with its bewildering array of switches was now familiar to her and after the first night of aching shoulders her muscles had become accustomed to the weight of heavy pots and pans.

That night she felt a lot less weary than usual. Relief maybe that the gruelling tasks were over, or could it be that physically she had become used to the work? By the time she reached the homestead, dinner was over and she took it that everyone was in the lounge room. She slipped up the hallway unnoticed or so she thought until the door of Drew's office was flung open and a masculine voice called, 'Come in here for a minute, will you, Lee?'

So, she thought, it was to be one of their employer and employee sessions. Since the night of her outburst of temper she had seen little of Drew. Secretly she felt a little ashamed of that split-second accusation of hers but she would never admit that to him. No doubt he was about to pay her the wages due for her week's work in the shed.

'Take a seat!' He had risen from his desk and was pushing forward a chair. Lee dropped down to face him across the desk. With a mere flick of his eyes he could raise such a torrent of feeling in her, she thought hotly. But of course it was inevitable after their last stormy encounter, and nothing that had happened since had given her cause to change her mind about the boss. *Or vice versa*, a dark goblin whispered deep in her mind.

'About your stint in the shed,' it was Drew at his most remote, eyes devoid of emotion, voice cool and impersonal. 'I've paid off the rest of the gang, now it's your turn. You're down on the wages sheet for award wages of course, plus allowances. You'll see it all there,' he handed her a slip of paper showing various figures.

Lee stared stupidly at the total, a sum far in advance of anything she had expected. 'This comes to thirty dollars a day!'

'That's right. I'll make you out a cheque.'

He had begun writing in his cheque book when she came to life. 'But there's no need!'

He glanced up enquiringly and something in his dispassionate gaze sent her thoughts spinning in confusion. 'I mean, I owe it to you, the fare money you lent me from Samoa. You told me you'd take it out of my wages when I got some work here.'

He was silent for a moment. It was the first time in their acquaintance that she had seen him in the slightest degree nonplussed. The next moment she told herself she had imagined the moment of indecision for he shot at her, 'All right then.' He cancelled the half-written cheque. 'If that's the way you want it!'

'It is.'

He sent her one of his penetrating glances and she was unhappily aware of hands red from dish-washing and arms marked with deep red burns. She hadn't used make-up for days, for what use was make-up in the blistering heat of the shed? And her hair? Beyond washing it in a shower at night and running a comb through in the morning she hadn't given it a thought all week. Why must she think of all this right at this moment? Chances were he wouldn't even notice her appearance.

She leaned forward across the desk, blue eyes wide and appealing as a child's. 'I've scarcely touched the rest of the money you lent me in Samoa and now that I can pay you back the fare money, I'll be able to save every cent with my next job.'

'Your next job?' If only his gaze weren't so cold and forbidding.

She rallied herself to say brightly, 'Why yes, that was the arrangement wasn't it? You were to find me some work so I could be on my way back to England. How much *is* the fare from here to London?'

'Somewhere around the eight hundred dollar mark at the moment.'

Eight hundred dollars! And she was starting from scratch. Still, she was good at saving money *and better at giving it away to someone like Jeremy, who had found it easy to take advantage of her too generous nature.* She thrust away the voice in her mind and said resolutely, 'All I need is a job!'

'Shearers' cook?' There it was again, the sardonic twist to his lips. If only he wasn't so darn good-looking it would be so much easier to hate him!

'Never! I've had that. But there must be something?'

'You didn't like it then?'

'Like it?' She gritted her teeth, and with an effort stopped the words that trembled on her lips. She wouldn't allow him to provoke her so easily this time. She forced a careless smile. 'Anyway, the gang didn't complain.'

'I told you they were easily pleased!'

Desperate for encouragement, Lee waited. Now was the moment for him to say: 'I have to admit you've made a fine job of it after all——' She waited . . . and waited. As the silence lengthened she told herself that one didn't have to be a mind reader to know he had no intention of offering her congratulations on her success as shearers cook. She must have been out of her mind even to think of such a thing happening. Oh, he made her feel so *angry!* He had that effect on her and no matter how they started out she finished up feeling furious with him! She tried to control the words that spilled from her lips. 'I'll have to find something to do,' she stated bluntly. 'Earn a bit more than this if I'm to get that fare back to London.'

Now was his opportunity to tell her that he had a job already lined up for her. He didn't say anything. He merely regarded her with the quizzical mocking glance that did things to her composure, made anger rise in a flood.

'That's right,' he conceded in the maddeningly soft tone that experience had shown her was Drew at his most deadly. Clearly the job he had promised her wasn't forthcoming and wildly she wondered just what he did want in return for her fare money and a way out of her dilemma. Apparently it wasn't work on the station. She couldn't understand him at all. It was the flicker of amusement in his eyes that sent her anger flying out of control. 'Look, I don't *have* to work for you! I've paid you back the money you lent me so we're quits!'

'Are we?' Still the soft accents.

She ignored his comment and swept on. 'I'll get a job somewhere else. A nursing auxiliary in a hospital. There must be hospitals over the country and nurses are always in demand——'

'How about a work permit?' he reminded her in his deceptively gentle tone. 'You won't get far without one and don't forget, you're not fully trained as a nurse and that can make all the difference when it comes to applying for a work permit here.'

Flung off her guard, she stared back at him, wide-eyed. 'How do you know?'

'I checked up on it.'

'You would,' she said in a low bitter tone.

He went on inexorably. 'This way you stay on here to all intents and purposes my guest, working for me until you get the fare home. I'll find you something to do. You'll just have to make the best of it. You can't get away.'

Lee's eyes glittered with anger. He blocked her at every turn, damn him! Flushed and defiant, she faced him. 'I won't be a prisoner on your sheep station!'

'You'll be anything I want!' He took a step towards her and at something in his gaze she stood frozen.

The next moment he had caught her close, his arms pinning her in so tight an embrace that she could feel his hard muscular chest pressed against her soft body. Through the mad confusion of her senses his lips came down on hers with hard pressure, then he released her so abruptly that she all but fell.

'Oh you——' Flushed and defiant, she faced him.

'And there'll be more of that if you don't behave yourself!'

After one startled glance in his direction Lee made for the door. It served her right she supposed, the thoughts whirled wildly through her mind as she hurried away, for crossing swords with him. Clearly the master of Mahia wasn't accustomed to being openly defied by one of his staff, but to take *that* manner of revenge! She passed the back of her hand across her lips in an unconscious gesture as if to brush away the memory of his punishing kiss.

Her mind programmed to a dawn start, Lee awoke early on the following morning, then realisation came with a rush. She had finished with her job of cooking for the shearing gang and she had got through it all, well, not too badly. At least Drew hadn't been able to find fault with her efforts. Somehow the thought gave her enormous satisfaction, almost as much as being able to lie abed for two more hours. Stretching her arms above her head, she reached for the paperback on a table by her bed. Such luxury!

It seemed strange, she thought a little later, to be going in for breakfast with the others. In the doorway she paused, surprised to find Drew here for usually he breakfasted with the men hours earlier. A brief nod in

Lee's direction and he resumed his conversation with Katrina, who appeared to be hanging on to every word he said. Was that the type of girl he preferred, she wondered, someone like his 'kitten', who gazed up at him with adoring eyes. All at once Lee wondered if the other girl were really as juvenile as she appeared. Could it all be an act to make Drew love her as he had loved that other woman? If so the plan seemed to be working well, she thought waspishly, judging by the indulgent half-smile on Drew's face as he inclined his dark head towards her.

'Look who's here!' David called across the table. 'I thought you were never going to get shot of that job of yours.' His appreciative glance swept Lee's young face. Her hair, curling around her forehead, was damp from a shower and she looked glowingly alive and at peace with the world—until she caught Drew's un-smiling gaze fixed on her.

Katrina intercepting his glance, sent him a provoca-tive look. 'Aren't you going to say something to Lee, Drew? Like what a success she made of the cooking—all that stuff?'

Lee cut in hurriedly. 'It was just a job. It was okay, once you got used to it.'

'Judging by the state of your hands,' David observed drily, his eyes fixed on the strips of Band-aid, 'it took a bit of getting used to.'

She threw him a smile, a dimple peeping at a corner of her mouth. 'Could be I was a bit careless. The knives in the kitchen over in the shed are awfully sharp when you're cutting up oodles of stew meat, and those shearers had good appetites.' How easy it was to smile about it all now.

David handed her a mug of coffee he had poured. 'So now you're free to have a look around the place. Do you realise,' he appealed to his mother, 'that Lee's been here for over a week and all she's seen of Mahia is the inside of the wool shed?' He smiled his charming smile. 'So how about it Lee? I can take you for a look around the place right after breakfast.'

'Aren't you forgetting something?' Drew's decisive tones cut across the boyish accents. 'How about that fencing job on the eastern boundary?'

David looked nonplussed for a moment. 'How about it?'

'You'd better get on with it. Lee won't mind if you can't make it.'

Well, of all the nerve! Lee opened her mouth to protest when Drew got lazily to his feet. 'Especially as I'll be taking her myself.'

'You might have asked me,' she muttered under her breath. Aloud she said, 'Don't bother going out specially for me!'

'Oh, but I'm not.' He regarded her with his hatefully bland expression. 'The boys are burning off some scrub up in the hills and I want to take a look-see. Might as well take you along with me.' He shot a glance towards David's mutinous face. 'Don't worry about David. He'll find lots to do on the block.'

'I'll bet.' David ground out the words between clenched teeth.

Jean was glancing from one son to the other. 'It doesn't matter who you go with,' she said to Lee. 'It's not as if it's anything special, just a sight-seeing tour!'

With Drew! Lee who five minutes earlier had felt so composed and happy, was now filled with conflicting emotions. That was the way Drew affected her, unfortunately. She suspected that for some cranky reason of his own, he had deliberately foiled his brother's plans. Even Katrina looked faintly surprised.

'You'll get used to the competition,' she told Lee. 'It's the shortage of girls up here in the never-never that makes us in such demand.' She gave a trill of laughter. 'Not that I'm complaining.'

Jean said laughingly, 'It's true you know.' Lee thought the older woman didn't appear to have caught the underlying sting in Katrina's words. 'You'll get used to it after a while.'

Drew spoke as if the subject were closed. 'I'll bring the Land Rover around at ten,' he told Lee.

'I'll come too, just for the ride,' Katrina said in her little-girl voice. 'There's nothing else around here to do today.'

'Sorry Kitten, not this time.' Drew made the position quite clear. 'With those storm clouds outside, we might cop heavy rain up in the hills. No sense in letting you in for a wetting too.'

Well! Lee thought indignantly. It seemed that Drew couldn't bear Katrina to be put to the slightest inconvenience but when it came to Lee—did he regard her merely as the shearers' cook? Before she could think up a sufficiently crushing retort he had got to his feet. 'Excuse me folks. See you later Lee.' He strode from the room.

Jean was looking towards Katrina in surprise. 'But I thought John was coming today and staying over the weekend for the dance?'

'Oh yes, so he is.' Katrina's lashes veiled her eyes. 'I almost forgot about him.'

Jean's eyes twinkled. 'He would never forget about you.'

'Oh John,' Katrina moved restlessly, 'he's just got a thing about me.'

'Sure has.' David appeared to have recovered his good humour. 'Whenever you're up here for a visit you can bet your life old John'll be along before long.' He shot her a teasing glance. 'Anyone would think you two were an engaged couple!'

'Oh shut up!'

Jean turned to Lee. 'Katrina and John have known each other since they were children. Their parents' farms aren't that far apart from each other, and they've been brought up practically like brother and sister.'

Katrina giggled. 'That's not exactly the way John sees it.' She put up a hand to touch the floss-like hair.

'It's your own fault,' David told her, 'you shouldn't encourage the poor guy.'

'Encourage him!' Katrina protested. 'I've told and told him that I don't want to get serious but he just won't take any notice.'

'Oh well, not to worry,' David said, 'you never know, he might take a fancy to some other girl at the dance at the weekend.' His laughing glance was on Lee's face. 'Someone new!'

'I don't think there's much danger of that.' Katrina's contemptuous glance swept Lee's round face and curly hair. 'He just can't see past me.'

To change the subject Lee said, 'Where is the dance being held? I didn't see a hall anywhere on the way here.'

'That's because there wasn't one,' David told her with a grin, 'It's right here in the wool shed. No need to polish the floor for dancing, it's slippery as hell already. It's amazing who turns up for a dance when the word gets around. 'Not my girl, worse luck, she's away nursing in town but I daresay I'll get by with a few substitutes, just for once.'

Lee was ready promptly at ten o'clock. Wearing well-worn denim jeans and a blue cotton T-shirt she went into the living room. A few moments later Mrs Mac came towards her. 'I've fixed you some sandwiches. When you take off with Drew you never can tell how long you'll be away, not with forty-nine miles of Land Rover tracks on the station!'

'Lovely.' As she took the box from the housekeeper, Lee couldn't help reflecting how swiftly she had changed from the position of a preparer of food to the receiving end, as it were. She strolled out to the verandah just as Drew drove up in the Land Rover.

She was still puzzled over the reason why he had asked her and not Katrina to accompany him but thinking about the matter made her feel angry all over again so she brushed the thought aside and hurried down the flight of steps.

Once in the vehicle, seated at Drew's side, her spirits lifted. What matter how devious and horrible the boss? She was in a country she would never see again and to her the surroundings were unfamiliar territory, wild and remote. They passed the grove of karaka trees behind the big woolshed and took a Land Rover track running up a steep rise. It was a direction that was new to her and glancing down she saw the turbulent sea of the coast and the steepness of the shoreline. They moved down a slope over another rise then she realised Drew had braked to a stop at a wide timber gate. He made no move to get out and after a moment or so she glanced towards him, a question in her eyes. 'Is something wrong?'

'No, no,' his tone was careless, 'nothing wrong.'

'Well then?'

'Just waiting,' he murmured patiently, 'for you to open the gate.'

'Me?' Whatever next would he ask of her, she wondered wildly? Well, he could wait for ever for all she cared. If he wanted the gate open he could open it himself.

'That's right.' He was leaning back, seemingly with all the time in the world. 'Round these parts it's an unwritten rule that the driver isn't the one who opens the gate.' He sent her an ironic grin. 'Passenger's privilege!'

'Privilege?'

'Well, duty if you like. Well, are you going to spring to it?'

She threw him a disbelieving look but something in his expression made her think there might really be some truth in what he said.

'Oh, all right then.' She leaped down to the dried grass and two minutes later she was still struggling with the stubborn catch. He didn't come to her rescue of course. He wouldn't, she thought crossly. All he did was to sit there with that hateful look of amusement on his face. Flushed and angry, she gave the catch a vicious wrench. To her surprise the gate swung open and she stood waiting while he drove the Land Rover through the opening. She had almost as much difficulty in shutting the gate behind him.

At last she flung herself back on the seat at his side. 'If you're having me on——'

'Would I do that?' His voice was bland. 'That was a tough catch to handle,' he conceded. 'The others aren't so bad and now that you've got the hang of it——'

She stared at him suspiciously, eyes bright with resentment. 'How many others?'

'Never counted them myself,' he murmured laconically and added cheerfully, 'but you'll find out.'

'I'll bet I will!'

All at once she realised they were approaching an airstrip over which she had ridden. Could it have been only a week or so ago? A small plane had landed on the grass and Drew drove towards it. In a few minutes he had braked to a stop beside the plane and had left Lee to go to speak with the pilot. He was back in a few minutes. 'The nor'wester is getting up and he's not too happy about the down draughts,' Drew told her.

'The pilot won't be working today then?'

'He'd be wasting his time if he did with the wind

blowing the dust away from the hillsides!' Drew put a hand to the starter motor.

A few minutes later she glanced back to see the small plane flying back in the direction from which it had appeared. Her gaze moved down steep green slopes where far below the sun struggling through banks of threatening grey cloud, gilded a magnificent sweep of coastline. Cloud shadows chased themselves over cleared hillsides as they climbed steep dried faces of station land then dropped down to follow a Land Rover track running down to a bush-filled ravine.

'A lot of acreage is still in scrub,' he told Lee, 'but this year I'm putting three hundred acres of hill country into grass. That's where the supermen, top-dressing pilots to you, come into the picture.'

'I see.' Dreamily she was thinking how attractive was his lean dark face and sensitive mouth. Who would believe that a man possessing such masculine magnetism that just to be near him made her feel acutely *aware* of him, could be guilty of such deliberate unpleasantness. Or could it be that it was only towards her that he betrayed the dark side of his nature?

They had been travelling a long time, it seemed to Lee, before she became aware of the acrid smell of smoke in her nostrils and all at once they came in sight of flames licking a steep hillside covered in densely growing, impenetrable manuka.

'The battle of the scrub,' Drew said. 'On the steep faces it has to be burned off, then sown by air.' He took a twisting path down the hillside and she waited in the vehicle while he made his way towards two burly figures almost obscured by a screen of rising smoke.

He came back before long and they were moving again, taking a twisting path winding up into the hills. A few miles further on he pulled up outside a rough timber hut. He must surely have forgotten momentarily who his passenger was she thought, for he turned to her with a grin. 'Coming in? Or aren't you hungry?'

She found she was hungry, very. As he flung open the door of the vehicle, wind tore at them and heavy drops of rain began to fall as they hurried towards the small shelter so far from civilisation.

'The boys use this place when they're mustering up in the hills,' he opened the door, 'Welcome to Possum Lodge.'

Inside the tiny building there was an open fireplace with firewood already laid and needing only a match to set it alight, a stretcher bed, supplies of tinned food on a shelf, a sink bench.

'It's something when you're miles from the homestead.' He put a match to the sticks and the flames blazed cheerfully and crackled on the dried wood. He went outside to fill a blackened billy with water from a nearby tank, then set the billy on the flames. He sent her a crooked grin. 'Hope you've got something to go with it!'

'Oh I can help you there.' She reached into her capacious bag and laid the packet of sandwiches on the table. 'Mrs Mac saw to that.'

'I can always count on her not to let me down.'

Not like me. Was she being super sensitive, Lee wondered, to take his remark as criticism of herself? It was absurd she told herself, to read an underlying significance into his words, to feel that in some ridiculous way, his opinion of her really mattered.

The rain was heavier now, slashing against the window pane and streaming down to the sill. Not that the window couldn't do with a wash, she thought irrelevantly and flicked away a spider's web with her handkerchief. She turned to meet Drew's deep compelling gaze and as their glances locked together she was aware of a powerful emotion flashing between them. With an effort she wrenched her glance aside, and said a little breathlessly, 'Cups? Shall I——'

'If you please.'

She must be careful not to let herself fall into that particular trap, she told herself. Enemy or no, there was a masculine magnetism about him against which she seemed to have no defence. At that moment lightning flared across her face, to be followed by a roll of thunder that reverberated in the hills around them. Inside the hut however they were sheltered and dry and the fire crackled merrily. Even Drew seemed to unbend a little, whistling a tune as he poured boiling water over tealeaves in a battered aluminium pot.

Lee found the 'club' sandwiches the housekeeper had prepared to be quite delicious. Home-made bread in slices was laid between layers of varied fillings— egg, tomato, chutney, cold meats—then sliced into finger length wedges.

She found herself listening with real interest as Drew spoke of the work that was his life. 'Mahia's just a narrow six-mile strip of coastal hill country, 7000 acres all told, with 2000 acres of it still in heavy bush.' Wide-eyed and intent soon she found herself lost in his account of a man's unending battle with the scrub on a back-country New Zealand sheep station. Something of her genuine interest in what he was telling her must have got through to him for he said in a tone that was friendly, well, almost, 'Anything you want to know about the place and what goes on at Mahia, just ask me.'

Lee stirred her tea thoughtfully. The temptation to take full advantage of his offer was proving very difficult to resist. 'All right then,' she took a deep breath, 'tell me, why did you bring me up here today? Was it because,' she flung at him, 'you didn't want your brother to take me around? You don't trust me one little bit, do you?'

'David?' The bewilderment in his expression told her she had made a dreadful mistake. 'I mean,' she added hastily, 'it's not as if you want to be bothered with me, not after . . .' Her voice trailed away at the memory of their meeting in his study last night.

'Just the usual thing,' somehow his flat tone was more deflating than the angry retort she had anticipated. 'We make a point of showing guests around the place.'

'But I'm not a guest!' She flashed back. 'You said so yourself——' She was interrupted by the opening of the door as on a flurry of wind and rain, the two men she had seen burning off scrub not far away, entered the room and slammed the door shut behind them.

'Reckon we've had it for today. This storm isn't going to blow over.' One of the men was shaking the raindrops from his hat.

'You're right there. This is Lee——' Drew made introductions then the talk became general.

The trip home was made in drenching rain and as a sight-seeing excursion Lee mused wryly, it was indeed a 'wash-out'. Shafts of lightning, playing over inky-black low-lying clouds, flashed across the windscreen at intervals and the boom and crash of breakers on the black sand of the coast below mingled with the swishing of tall trees bending in gale force winds and rain pelting down on the roof of the Land Rover.

At any other time the sheer precipitous slopes they were taking would have filled Lee with alarm but the sight of Drew's firm hand on the steering wheel, the casual tone of his voice as he threw an occasional word over his shoulder to the men in the back seat, was infinitely reassuring. Once as they swung around a bush-lined bend, a tall tree struck by a shaft of lightning, came crashing to the ground but apart from Drew's laconic 'Lucky it fell the right way or we'd have had to get out and clear the track' no one took much notice. Drew . . . her thoughts wandered. Once he found work for her at Mahia as he had promised, she would be able to save her entire wages, for here in the outback there were no attractive stores to tempt one to buy fashion garments or cosmetics. No one here was interested in her appearance anyway.

At that moment there came unbidden to her mind a smiling, masculine face. She was grateful to Paul. He had made all the difference to her having got through her ordeal in the shed but she doubted if she would see him again, even if she wanted to. Right now life for her was simplified into one main objective and that was to escape from Drew Hamilton's clutches and get back to England. Once there, she wondered, would all this seem like a dream? Involuntarily her glance went to Drew's strong profile. Rain had misted his clear tanned skin and his gaze was on the twisting path lost a short way ahead in the blurred outlines of the bush. Lee's soft lips firmed. Forget Drew Hamilton, after the high-handed treatment she had been forced to endure at his hands? She only wished she could!

CHAPTER SIX

WHEN they reached the house Lee noticed a long red mud-spattered car standing in the driveway. 'Looks as though John's made it through the storm,' Drew commented. 'Oh well, it makes a difference, I guess, having an incentive.'

She sent him a quick look. Was he feeling some jealousy at the arrival of the other man? she wondered. A man who, it seemed, was deeply in love with Katrina. If so, he hid his emotions well, his tone as laconic and offhand as usual—but then, she reminded herself, with Drew you never could tell. That was the one thing she had learned about him, apart from his ruthlessness, his crushing irony, and these attributes seemed only to apply in dealings with her. It was very odd.

A little later, showered and wearing a dress of soft blue cotton, she went into the lounge room. Music from the stereo pulsed through the room. Drew must have gone outside to see to the stock, she thought, but Katrina looked happy enough. She was curled up on the carpeted floor sorting through records, a sturdily built young man at her side. He got to his feet as Lee came into the room.

'Hi!' His puzzled expression told Lee that Katrina had made no mention of the shearers' cook.

Now, however, in one swift glance, the other girl was taking in Lee's face, the satiny English skin, glowing still from her shower, the simple blue dress that highlighted the colour of her eyes, the dainty high-heeled white sandals that lent her height. Anyone would think, the way she's staring at me, Lee told herself, that she'd never seen me before.

'John . . . Lee,' Katrina said shortly.

There was something straightforward and likeable in the tanned boyish face, his clear-eyed look as he took her hand in a crushing grip. 'Katrina didn't tell me——' His appreciative glance said the rest.

'Lee's the shearers' cook,' Katrina told him, 'or at least, she was.' There was a gleam of malice in the wide eyes. 'Have you got another job yet, Lee? You should put your name down for a replacement. You might be lucky enough even to land a job doing the circuit with one of the shearing gangs.'

Lee laughed. 'I might, but I'm not going to try. Not for me! I never knew,' she appealed smilingly to John, 'that work could be like that!'

'Tough, eh?' He studied her consideringly. 'I take it it was just a try-out—you're not a journalist, by any chance, getting experience of the real thing so you can write it up afterwards?'

Lee dropped to a low stool, hands linked around her knees. 'Not me.'

'I didn't think,' John still looked puzzled,' you looked like a working girl.

'Oh, but I am!' A shadow of anxiety crossed her face. 'Now that my shearing stint is over, I'm on the look-out for a job right now.'

'What type of work did you have in mind?'

Lee shrugged her shoulders. 'I don't mind. I gather it's not always easy to find work in the country.'

He grinned. 'Does it have to be the country?'

The unanswerable question. A mental picture of Drew's sardonic face shot into her mind. In the lengthening silence she searched her mind wildly for an answer, but all she came up with was a lame, 'I—I like it here.' The next moment her temporarily paralysed brain swung back into action. 'It's such a change for me,' she chattered wildly, 'It's so remote, and being a stranger to this country——'

'She's a Pom,' Katrina cut in succinctly.

Lee ignored the mocking voice. 'I'm getting a good idea of the back country,' she felt proud of her use of the New Zealand term, 'and the top-dressing the planes are doing on the hills and everything.'

Apparently John was satisfied with Lee's reasons for wishing to remain in a country district. Katrina, looking bored, was plainly not interested in the matter.

'At home in England,' Lee went on, 'I used to do auxiliary nursing in a convalescent hospital.' A dimple peeped at the corner of her mouth. 'But I can't see myself getting anything in that line around here. Everyone seems so healthy.'

'You'd be surprised.' John seemed to be warming to his subject and Katrina's small mouth took on a petulant twist. 'It's just about the hardest thing in the world to get any help in the domestic line out here in the back of beyond. Can't blame the girls for preferring to be in a city or at least in a small town where they can see a bit of life, take in a Saturday night disco, or see the latest movie. If you're really serious about wanting work——'

'Oh, I am!' The expression of interest in Lee's eyes underlined her words.

'It's my sister really.' He was speaking in a thoughtful tone. 'She——'

Katrina had put a pop melody on the turntable and suddenly the lilting notes filled the room. She looked up at John with her appealing gaze. 'Come on, let's dance!' She tugged impatiently at his arm.

'In a minute.' At Katrina's astounded expression Lee suspected it was the first time ever that John had failed to spring to do her bidding.

'Michelle and her husband are living at home at the

moment,' he told Lee. 'Our place isn't so far from here as distances go in the outback. The thing is, Michelle's expecting the arrival of twins pretty soon. She spends half her time putting ads in the local rag trying to find a girl to give her a hand for the first few months. Her doctor is doing his best to locate someone, but so far,' he spread his hands in a helpless gesture, 'no luck! Gee,' he regarded Lee even more warmly than when he had first set eyes on her, 'if you could help out for a few months, she'd be more than grateful!'

She glanced up at his eager young face. 'How long——'

'She goes into hospital next week.'

Lee's smile was straight from the heart. 'But that's wonderful! It might just work out for both of us. Would you tell your sister I'll come and see her——' She stopped short as Drew strode into the room.

'Good to see you, John.' Drew was a master hand at hiding his true feelings, she thought. She would give him that. He moved to the cocktail cabinet in a corner of the room. 'No slips on the road on the way here?'

'Not when I shot through, but since then there are probably wash-outs all along the track.'

Lee found herself wishing John would go on talking. It gave her a chance to study Drew without his being aware of her scrutiny. Wearing fawn-coloured cords and cream turtleneck sweater, he looked, she had to admit, very, very attractive. That straight back, the way he carried himself.

'What'll you have Lee? A sherry?' She realised he was looking at her enquiringly and she coloured slightly.

'Please.'

'I know what you like, Katrina. John?'

'Beer for me, thanks.'

When Drew had brought the drinks he dropped to a

low chair, studying the whisky in his glass. Then his gaze moved to the window where rain streamed down. The sea was blotted out in a curtain of mist and a flash of lightning lighted up the window. 'If this keeps on we'll have to move the ewes to higher ground. The storm will be all over by the time you go back,' he said to John.

'And that won't be long!' Katrina got to her feet, and eyes flashing and head held high, marched out of the room.

John's face fell. For a moment he made as if to follow her, then subsided in the seat.

'What's wrong?' Drew was watching him in some amusement.

'Nothing much. I guess,' a selfconscious smile touched John's lips, 'she's used to demanding all the attention, and getting it.' He emptied his glass. 'Lee and I have just been getting to know each other. I didn't even know she was here.'

'It was a snap decision,' Drew said smoothly. 'We both happened to be over in Samoa at the same time. I'd stopped over on the flight home from England to look up my sister Beverley. You remember Bev?'

John nodded.

'Lee comes from England and wanted to see around New Zealand, especially the back country. It seemed a good idea,' Drew said lazily, 'to invite her up here for a look around.'

'Is that the way of it?' John looked bewildered, as well he might, Lee thought, her lips twitching in secret amusement. Which girl, John must be wondering, is the real Lee? The hardworking, hard-up shearers' cook or the footloose tourist travelling half a world away just to 'take a look around' an unfamiliar country?

Evidently, Lee thought as she watched John's face,

his sister's desperate need for domestic help in the near future had won the day, for he was saying to Drew, 'Lee was telling me she was on the look-out for a job. I happen to know of something that would suit her at our place. When my sister comes out of hospital with the twins—that's the latest news at home—she'll really be needing help in the nursery department, so——'

'No!' Drew's staccato interruption startled both Lee and John. He rose and went to the cocktail cabinet, his back turned to them. 'Sorry,' he said in a milder tone, 'but it's just not on!'

The eager light died away from John's open face, but evidently, Lee thought, he wasn't giving up without a struggle. 'You did say,' he appealed to Lee, 'that you'd be willing to take it on?'

Before she could make a reply Drew answered for her and the deep decisiveness of his tones told them both that he meant business.

'You must have forgotten, Lee. You did promise me you'd take on that special employment I'm jacking up for you? We discussed it last night, remember?'

The thoughts tumbled wildly through her mind. True, he had spoken as if he were arranging something for her even though he hadn't mentioned any specific work. If she defied him in the matter she wouldn't put it past him to ring the proper authorities and make mention of a necessary work permit, thus putting an end to her employment with anyone but himself and making things very unpleasant for her. She would never get back to England that way. There really wasn't any alternative, she thought frustratedly, somehow there never was with Drew!

'I guess you're right.' She turned to John and had no need to pretend disappointment. 'Drew is arranging something for me and I did agree to it. Maybe you'll be able to find someone to help out with the babies yet.'

His face had fallen. 'I doubt it. Well,' he said on a sigh, 'I guess that's the way the cookie crumbles.'

Lee, taking in Drew's dark expression, his firmly set lips, longed to explain to John how very much she would have preferred to take his offer, if only she could. Once again she got the feeling of being held prisoner here. It was Drew who made her feel that way, he enjoyed having her in his power, darn him!

Katrina was still noticeably cool towards John when the family gathered together at the dinner table that evening. But she had problems enough of her own, Lee mused, without worrying about John's unhappiness. Problems like Drew's incredibly high-handed handling of the employment John had offered her. Drew didn't like her, he could scarcely bear to have her around his home, yet when an opportunity had presented itself for her to work somewhere else, he had behaved in that insufferable authoritative manner and forced her to turn the offer down. There was just no understanding him!

They had just begun the meal and John and Drew were discussing a recent stock sale in the district when Jean was called to the phone. She made a face in Mrs Mac's direction. 'Can't they ring again?'

'It's a toll call from Palmerston North, the hospital——'

'The hospital—that's different!' Jean rose and hurried away from the table. When she returned after a few minutes, everyone watched her curiously and Drew asked, 'What's the trouble?'

'It's your Aunt Edith.' Jean looked abstracted. 'I had to think fast that time! Seems she had an accident almost two weeks ago, fell and broke her hip. I do wish someone had let us know—but anyway, she's in hospital, the break has been set and everything's going along satisfactorily in that way. Now she's due to be sent home from hospital in a week's time, but of course she's all alone in her house. Of course I insisted on her coming to us and she was so pleased, said she would try and arrange for a nurse to come and help out, but she didn't think she'd have much success in that direction. I hope you don't mind,' she turned to Lee, 'but I took a chance and recommended you for the job, told her there was no need to worry herself looking for some other girl as we had someone here who's on the look-out for just that sort of work. There wouldn't be a great deal of work involved,' she added quickly. 'It's just that Aunt Edith won't be mobile for a while yet and she'll have to rest up most of the time.' She hesitated, eyeing Lee a trifle uncertainly. 'I hope I did the right thing? I suppose I should have asked you about it first, but you did say——'

'No, no, no, you did quite right. I'll take it on, of course I will!' Lee tried to speak calmly, but underneath her thoughts were rioting in a wild sense of triumph. Looking after the boss's elderly aunt, the very eventuality he had told her he would never allow.

She couldn't quite subdue the wicked glee dancing in her eyes as she looked up at Drew, seated opposite to her at the table. 'Is that okay with you, Drew?' she asked innocently.

It was impossible to read his deadpan expression. 'It's a bit late to change things now, anyway. It's up to you.'

Jean looked at him with surprise. 'But surely,' she cried incredulously, 'you wouldn't want to——'

'Like I said, it's up to Lee.'

'Oh, I don't mind!' Lee assured him blithely. She could scarcely believe in her good fortune. After all the battles she had had with this man, battles which he invariably won, fate had handed her an unexpected victory.

If Drew were irritated by the turn of events, however, he soon recovered himself, she decided a few minutes later, watching him as he laughed and talked with the others, responding goodnaturedly to Katrina's chatter and teasing her unmercifully in return. Hadn't she once read somewhere that for a man to tease a girl indicated that he was secretly in love with her? She wondered if the same thought had occurred to John. Certainly his downcast face showed no joy.

'I scarcely see anything of you these days.' Katrina sent Drew a reproachful look from beneath darkened lashes. 'I don't know why I come here to stay, you're always so busy!'

'To get away from home, of course,' he grinned, 'what else? How have you been amusing yourself all day, kitten?'

She pouted. 'Nothing very exciting. Talking to David, waiting for John to arrive. *You* were away for hours!'

'Oh, come now,' he leaned back in his chair, 'you don't need me around.'

'Don't I?' Her eloquent gaze said the rest.

Did Drew really think of Katrina as an engaging child whom he had seen grow up, Lee wondered, or could it be he was so sure of her infatuation for him that he could afford to treat her as a child? Either way the situation was very hard on John, sitting silently at Katrina's side and no doubt not tasting a morsel of the food he was pushing around on his plate. If only she hadn't been the cause of the present rift between them!

As the meal progressed, Drew's sudden change of mood made him unusually expansive towards everyone at the table. Even David, who more often than not incurred his elder brother's displeasure on account of a lack of interest in his work, came in for his share of good feeling. 'I heard on the grapevine,' Drew remarked, 'that you managed to get hold of a couple of musicians for the dance tomorrow night. How did you do it?'

David grinned lightheartedly. 'No problem when you've got the right contacts, brother.'

'Trust you for that!'

What could have happened, Lee wondered, to have put the boss in this affable mood? Could it possibly have anything to do with her staying on here to help with his aunt? What if he imagined he had scored a victory over her just at a time when he had forced her to refuse John's offer of employment? If that was the way he was thinking . . . The only course was to go to Drew herself and demand an explanation.

She waited until the meal had come to an end and Drew had gone to his office, then she tapped at the closed door. 'It's me, Lee!'

'Come in!'

She slipped into the room where he sat at his desk, stock sheets spread out before him. Closing the door behind her, she stood facing him. The blue dress was giving her an unaccustomed feeling of confidence when dealing with the boss. Or maybe it was the mere offer of employment when she had imagined such a thing to be out of the question, that was giving her courage.

'So it's you again!'

If only, just for once, he would seem pleased to see her, treat her in the way in which he would greet any other guest staying in his home. What a hope! She took a deep breath and rushed into speech. 'About that nursing job I've taken on, looking after your aunt when she comes——'

'Oh, that,' he appeared to be more interested in the stock sheets spread out on the desk. At last he condescended to regard her with his cool stare. 'It's paid employment. You'll be drawing the same wages you would if you worked in a hospital, plus allowances for living out of town, uniform——'

She brushed the matter aside impatiently. 'I don't care about all that!'

He raised thick dark eyebrows. 'Don't care? But I got the impression——'

'Well, I need the money, of course. You know all about that.' She took a step nearer to the desk. 'What I want to know is——'

'Sit down, Lee.'

She dropped to the seat on the opposite side of the big desk, then wished she hadn't. She had felt much more able to do battle with Drew when she was standing. Now she was so much nearer to him and there was an expression in his eyes that was definitely unnerving. It was like being hypnotised, she thought wildly. She had almost forgotten what she had come for. With an effort she wrenched her gaze aside. 'How did you know,' she burst out, 'that your aunt would be needing someone to help her when she comes here? Your mother had only just taken the message at dinnertime.'

'Actually I didn't know.' He studied her flushed face.

She raised perplexed blue eyes. 'But you said——'

'I said I'd jack up a job for you and you've got one. What's wrong with that?'

'Nothing at all, only——' She was finding it hard to concentrate. Blame his hatefully bland look. 'But you didn't have anything for me, not when you made me turn down John's offer to help his sister with her twins, when they arrive.' The words tumbled breathlessly from her lips.

'Did I tell you,' he demanded remorselessly, 'that I had anything specific lined up for you right now?'

'No, but——'

'I would have found you something to do before long. If not this, then something else would have turned up.'

'No,' she agreed bitterly, 'you certainly wouldn't have chosen this way out of the problem!' She heard her own voice rising high out of control. 'Or isn't your aunt a helpless old lady whom I might easily take advantage of?' She was breathing fast and the silence seemed to go on for ever.

Surprisingly, Drew smiled, only it was the twisted ironic tilt of the lips he seemed to keep just for her. 'My aunt would hardly thank you for that description of her! I think you'll find,' he added coldly, 'that she's fairly good at looking after herself.'

Something drove her on to goad him. 'Are you going to warn her—about me?'

His tone was very quiet. 'Do I need to?'

Their glances clashed and held and once again she found herself powerless to combat the electric excitement flashing between them. Fighting the waves of dizzying emotion that were all but submerging her, she swallowed, turning away. 'So long as I know!' she flung at him, and made her escape.

It was only later, lying in bed in the quietness of her upstairs room, that she asked herself what she had been escaping *from*. The scorching memory of his threat, 'If you don't behave yourself there'll be more of that!' still burned in her mind. Or could it be that she was fleeing from herself? She didn't dare pursue the matter to its logical conclusion for fear of what the answer might be.

CHAPTER SEVEN

THE following day found the womenfolk of the station caught up in preparations for the woolshed dance that night.

Katrina, unable to decide as to which dress she would wear to the dance, had on three occasions emerged from her bedroom, each time wearing a different evening dress, her long blonde hair arranged in a variety of styles. Ignoring Lee, Katrina appealed to Jean for her opinion in the matter.

On the last occasion Jean, busy on the telephone as she spoke with various friends in the district, answered a little impatiently. 'Why ask me? They all look gorgeous on you—but then,' she smiled wryly, 'I must confess that every girl your age looks beautiful to me whatever she wears. It's something to do with being past forty-five!'

'Oh, if you're not interested——' Katrina flung herself away.

Jean called after her, 'I am really, but they all look super to me. I don't see that it makes any difference.' As Katrina's eyes sparkled with annoyance once again, Jean added placatingly: 'Why not ask John what he thinks?'

'He's out with Drew,' Katrina spoke huffily. 'Tells me he can't wait to see me, then takes off the minute he can get away.'

Which wasn't fair, Lee thought, considering the contemptuous way in which Katrina had treated John last night. Hadn't she made it clear she had no wish to see him? Really, there was no pleasing the girl!

'Anyway,' Katrina complained, 'what's the use of asking him? He never gives me an honest opinion, just keeps telling me I look fantastic whatever I wear!'

'And what's wrong with that?'

'Oh, you never understand!' Katrina wailed, and flounced away in the direction of her room. No doubt, Lee mused, for the purpose of trying out yet another hair-style, for Katrina couldn't surely possess any more evening gear. At least that was one problem she didn't have to contend with, Lee thought wryly, not with the simple black number she had bought at C. & A. Stores in London especially for her overseas trip.

Idly she wandered into the kitchen. In spite of the heat of the electric range, the room was fresh and airy, a breeze stirring the yellow curtains at the windows. Mrs Mac, her apron as spotless as ever, was taking a massive pizza pie from the oven and arranging it on the bench alongside piles of small savouries, cream-filled eclairs and cheese straws.

'May I?' Lee helped herself to a straw and Mrs Mac nodded a grudging assent. 'Could I do anything to help?' Lee asked.

'I can manage. I always have.' The housekeeper's somewhat severe face had an expression of concentration and Lee got the impression she wasn't welcome in the kitchen just now.

In the hall she ran into Jean. 'Want any help?' Lee enquired.

'Oh, would you?' Jean thrust shears and a flat wicker basket she was carrying towards Lee. 'Be a dear and cut some flowers from the garden for me, will you? We'll need lots of hydrangeas and carnations. Hibiscus too, they won't last beyond the night, but no matter! Oh, and some of those tall blue flowers in the border too, agapanthus they're called. I'll be wanting greenery to go with them, but we can get that from the bush down in the gully.

'I'll get it for you,' Lee volunteered. 'I want to take a ride anyway.'

'That's wonderful!' Jean was looking slightly harassed. 'Heavens, I'll never get through in time! Better take a strong knife with you for cutting ferns and get lots of creepers, anything you can find that's decorative.'

Half an hour later, having gathered armfuls of flowers from the garden and plunged them deep in buckets of cold water, Lee made her way up a grassy slope to a hill paddock where she caught her mount and led the mare back to the stables. She was throwing a saddle on Gypsy's broad back when Ernie came ambling towards her, a grin on his weathered face. He eyed her appreciatively. 'Do-it-yourself job, eh? Didn't take you long to catch on.'

Lee laughed, struggling a little to buckle the girth. 'That's because Gypsy's so easy to catch. If she'd decided to gallop madly around the paddock for hours instead of being easily bribed with a carrot, I'd still be up the hill doing a marathon!'

He gave her a leg up into the saddle. 'Heard a rumour that you're planning to stay on working for the boss, only it's a sort of nursing job this time?'

Lee sent him a smile. 'It's true. I used to do that sort of work back in England, looking after convalescent folk.'

Ernie straightened himself. 'Thought there must be something in it. The boss was a bit close-mouthed on the subject. He didn't seem to want to discuss it and the boys asked me to get the low-down on it.'

Lee dimpled. 'You can tell them you have it straight from the horse's mouth, so to speak!'

'Don't worry, I'll pass it on. Don't mind telling you the boys have taken a liking to you. I guess it's because,' Lee barely caught the low tone, 'you're a bit different from some of the hoity-toity females we have to put up with around here. Wonder why the boss was so cagey about it?'

'Don't ask me!' But she had no need to wonder on that point, she knew. She could well imagine the boss's reaction to a situation where he now found himself compelled by family loyalties to offer her the one job in the world he would never have chosen.

Lee started off across the paddock and presently she was out on the hillside, a fresh wind blowing from the turbulent sea. She knew the fine black sand would be in her clothes and hair, but it was worth it all to feel the wind on her face as she rode up a winding track.

At the summit she reined in, gazing over the ranges and a long sweep of coastline. The scene was remote and lonely here at the end of the world. Yet for some reason she couldn't fathom, she was coming to love this unfamiliar life. Odd . . . She shrugged the puzzling thoughts aside and turned Gypsy down a track worn by a thousand sheep that led to a bush-filled gully between the hills.

In the sun-splashed clearing she left Gypsy to graze on the grass while she gathered armfuls of red rata flowers from the trees growing at the edge of the clearing. Presently she pushed her way between thickly-growing undergrowth and long black ropes of supplejack trailing from tall trees. From somewhere high above she caught the musical notes of a tui, and all around her was the cool damp smell of moss and ferns. She was struggling unsuccessfully to cut a vine when heavy steps sounded through the densely growing bush.

'Hi there!' a voice called, and she turned a surprised face to John, who came crashing towards her through the undergrowth.

'Am I glad to see you! All these gorgeous ferns and they're too tough for me to cut. Could you——'

'You want decorations for the woolshed dance tonight? How about this? And this?' Taking a knife from the sheath at his belt, he swiftly slashed trails of greenery. 'Let me go ahead!'

They went deeper into the bush, heavy with the pungent smell of damp earth. At first Lee was horrified when John cut the fronds of young punga trees, but as he pointed out, there were swags of pungas in the gully and it was the usual thing when there was anything on in the woolshed, to shove the fronds in corners. 'Makes things look a bit festive!' he told her.

It was a long time before they retraced their steps, Lee with her arms overflowing with greenery and John trailing trees and ferns with him. Time had gone by on wings, Lee thought, glancing with surprise at her wristwatch and relieved to see that the horses were still quietly grazing.

As they emerged into full sunlight, a horseman cantered by on the ridge above and she recognised Drew's easy seat. No doubt he had taken in the sight of the two people emerging from the bush. There was really no reason for her to feel selfconscious in the matter, yet somehow a little of the golden sparkle of the morning drained away. For heaven's sake, she scolded herself, she and John had only been gathering greenery together! So long, a niggling voice deep in her mind reminded her, as Drew takes that view of it. Stupid of her to feel this way, as if it mattered one little bit what Drew thought.

Shaking the leaves and twigs from her hair, Lee waited while John roped the young trees in front of his saddle. He put out a hand to help her as she climbed up on Gypsy, the sack in front of her filled with greenery. They rode back together, taking their time on the precipitous slopes. When they had unsaddled their mounts and rubbed them down they went to the house. John tossed the punga fronds and nikau palms down in the shade, but Lee lugged her bag of creepers, branches and rata flowers in at the back door.

'It's me—Lee!' she called to Jean, but it was Katrina who came strolling down the hall to meet them, her small mouth pursed crossly, her glance, heavy with suspicion, moving from Lee to John.

'So I see.'

John said, 'We met down in the gully and Lee asked me to give her a hand with the decoration stuff. Some of those ferns take a heck of a lot of yanking out.'

'*Really?*'

Lee could have told John that he was wasting his time in pursuing the subject, for clearly Katrina had made up her mind to all manner of wild fancies. As she left them and went in search of Jean, Lee reflected that in her present mood of jealousy and resentment Katrina would be apt to seize on any pretext to punish John for daring to show interest in any other girl but herself. But jealousy implied a degree of caring. Was it possible—the next minute she recalled Katrina's utter absorbtion in the boss. No, the other girl might be piqued by someone who was her devoted slave daring to be friendly with another girl, but that would be all. Drew was the man Katrina was crazy about, anyone could see that. Lee couldn't understand why she found the thought so depressing.

That afternoon found John scrubbing the table in the woolshed and sweeping the floor. Jean, with the help of Lee and Katrina, arranged trails of greenery on the makeshift stage, slipping scarlet and pink hibiscus blossoms among the ferns. Later, John carried in punga fronds and nikau palms, standing them in corners and at intervals along the walls. He had finished laying long planks of timber on hay bales for seating when Katrina told him stiffly, 'You don't need to stay any longer now.'

John hesitated. Plainly, Lee thought, he would like to find an excuse, any excuse, to mend the rift between himself and Katrina. At last, however, he turned away. 'Okay, if that's the way you feel!' Lee, who was feeling slightly guilty on his account, took in his downcast face. She jumped down from a hay bale on which she had been standing and arranged a trailing vine along the wall. 'Maybe you'll have better luck at the dance tonight,' she whispered.

'You reckon?' He sent her a determined grin and gave her a thumbs-up sign.

It was a hot night with grey clouds massing over the hills and even the breeze from the sea failed to cool the humid air. Much too hot a night, Lee decided, for the close-fitting black dance dress she had brought with her from London. All at once she remembered she had a choice of garments. On an impulse she slipped over her head the cream muslin dress with its floating butterfly sleeves that she had purchased at the hotel shop in Samoa and worn only once, on the night of the island barbecue. She ran a comb through her hair until it fluffed around her face in soft curls, then slipped around her lightly tanned throat the shell pendant she had bought from a native boy in Apia. Why not? The outfit was cool and comfortable on a hot night. In their enervating humidity of the Pacific island, the Polynesian people certainly knew the most suitable wear for comfort, she decided, stooping to tie the ankle cords of her woven string sandals.

Pausing for a last glance in the mirror, she reflected that tonight she looked her best. The only thing was, she thought wryly, who was she looking her best *for*? The only man at the dance whom she knew at all well would be Drew, and he wouldn't care in the least what she looked like. He might not even dance. He hadn't joined in the dancing on the grass at the island barbecue, she remembered. And as to dancing with her, why should he? He would have his 'kitten' gazing at him with adoring eyes as well as heaven only knew how many of the local girls! Probably, she mused with an odd clutch of the heart, he won't even notice I'm there. Just then a peremptory rap sounded on the door, and only one person in the house she knew, would knock in that no-nonsense manner. Lee gave herself a moment to school her voice to a note of careless surprise, then opened the door, to come face to face with Drew, tall, erect, oddly unfamiliar in a cream silk overshirt and immaculate fawn slacks. For a moment something flickered in his eyes, a light she had never seen there before, and for a crazy moment she found herself regretting having worn the island frock that would immediately take him back to Samoa and the disturbing circumstances of their first meeting.

'All ready?' he was saying.

'I guess so.' She tried out her careless smile and said the first thing that came into her mind. 'Do I look all right for the dance, in this?'

To her surprise he didn't seem to notice her Samoan-style dress. His gaze was sweeping the apricot tan of her throat, moving upwards to her defiant young face. 'You look all right to me,' he drawled. 'I'll take you over to the shed.' Ordinary enough words, yet something in his tone sent a flare of excitement through her.

'Thanks.' She had expected to go to the dance with the family party and wondered at Drew's unexpected solicitude for her. There was bound to be a reason for his seeking her out, she told herself, trying for composure, and no doubt she would find out the explanation before the night was over. She stole a glance at his face and found his eyes meeting hers. A tiny shock ran through her. What could have happened to change him so much tonight? There was a contained excitement in his eyes—and something else. Had she not had good cause to know better, almost she could have put it down to an unexpected tenderness.

At the foot of the stairs he paused. 'Lee, there's something——' She glanced up at him enquiringly, but he said, 'Forget it! Tell you later!' She realised that Jean, looking amazingly attractive in a crimson caftan, was beckoning to Drew. 'Are you going over to the shed now? The others aren't ready yet, so I'll come along with you.' Her eyes crinkled in a smile. 'I know Lee won't mind.'

'Of course not.' But deep down she wasn't so sure on that point. Just now Drew had seemed to her to be a different man entirely from the one she knew—alive, excited, interested in *her*! If by some miracle he came to care for her, *really* care, what an opportunity she would have to take her revenge on him! The next moment she pulled herself up, aghast at the direction in which her thoughts were leading. Drew in love with her merely because he had sent her a glance that wasn't altogether disapproving? What could be the matter with her to imagine such things?

She wrenched her mind back to the present and soon they were moving down the verandah steps and climbing into the Land Rover for the short drive to the woolshed. The last of the daylight was fading and a few faint stars pricked the luminous blue of the sky. Around them the hills were bathed in purple shadows. The wind of the day had died away and the sound of the sea was muted.

When they reached the lighted wool shed, Drew parked the vehicle among a cluster of trucks, cars and Land Rovers standing at haphazard angles on the dried grass. People were getting out of vehicles, doors slammed and Lee caught echoes of Drew's name as friends greeted one another. Everyone seemed to know everyone else, except herself, Lee mused as Drew took her arm impersonally and led her up the high steps.

Inside, she found the shed to be a scene of activity. On the makeshift stage with its backdrop of flowers and greenery, two young Maori musicians were seated on hay bales as they idly strummed their guitars. Friends gathered in groups to talk eagerly together in the manner of people living in an isolated part of the country. A few children slid excitedly up and down the oil-slippery floor.

Jean said: 'You know, Lee, I don't think you've met the wives of the two shepherds living on the station. You've been too busy up till now.' She guided Lee towards a laughing, chattering group. 'Here they are, together as usual. Lee, this is Jan—and Robyn.'

Jan, an animated dark-haired girl with a merry smile, said gaily, 'We have to be friends with each other, Robyn and I, seeing that apart from Jean, we're the only women living permanently at Mahia.'

'And we've both got young children who keep us rather tied,' Robyn, a tall fair girl with a shy manner, put in. 'We give each other moral support when it all gets one or other of us down.'

'It works in very well actually,' Jan told Lee. 'Like tonight. But we do sometimes feel like getting away.'

Lee said, 'Why don't you——'

Jan made a wry face. 'Take a holiday, you mean? With two young children? And a mother who happens to live away in the South Island?'

Lee couldn't help the thought that for all their complaints, the two girls seemed happy and contented with life at Mahia.

'It's all a matter of love,' Jan was saying laughingly. 'If you're nuts about the guy it doesn't really make any odds where you live! You're together and that's all that matters.' Her glance softened as she eyed the stocky young man standing among a group of men. At that moment her husband sent her a grin and a wave of his hand. With a smile, Jan appealed to Lee, 'See what I mean?'

Lee nodded. Why did her gaze go straight to Drew, whose tall figure seemed to dominate the group of men? Drew of all men, who couldn't stand having her around the place. She really must stop herself thinking of him all the time, it was getting to be a habit with her. Only because of his hateful treatment of her, of course.

At that moment she became aware of a sudden hush in the babel of talk and laughter. Everyone was gazing towards the entrance doors where Katrina, on a wave of laughter, had arrived. She was accompanied by John and as the couple paused in the opening, Lee stood spellbound with the others. For in contrast with the more conventionally attired girls in the big room, Katrina stood out like a lovely tropical flower. Barefooted, and wearing the flowing Pacific Island muslin dress that Drew had brought her back from Samoa, she had let the long curtains of hair flow around her shoulders and had tucked among the blonde tresses, a pink hibiscus blossom. As if on cue, the guitarists broke into one of the traditional melodies of the Pacific islands and the haunting strains of *Isa Lei* stole through the room.

At that moment Katrina caught sight of Lee. The laughter froze on her face and she shot Lee a glance of barely concealed fury. Lee supposed that by wearing her own Polynesian-styled dress she had unwittingly ruined the other girl's moment of impact, but to her it didn't matter particularly. Indeed, she suppressed a wild desire to giggle. Clearly, though, it mattered terribly to Katrina.

Under cover of the throbbing guitars and soft Maori voices taking up the melody, Lee caught Jan's whisper. 'Robyn, you've had a holiday in the Pacific islands. Isn't a flower tucked behind a girl's ear sup-posed to say something significant?'

Robyn giggled. 'Just that you're looking for a boy-friend.'

'Well, well,' Jan pursed her lips, 'and with John back in attendance too!'

'Maybe,' Robyn murmured thoughtfully, 'it isn't John she's wanting. Could be it's another man, someone more ... interesting.' Speculatively both girls eyed Drew's tall figure.

At that moment Katrina and John took the floor, moving in time with the dreamy rhythm. For a few minutes the crowd was content to watch them, Kat-rina's shell necklaces flying out as she danced. Then the group of men gathered together in the doorway broke up and couples moved to swell the ever-growing crowd on the floor.

As the tempo changed to that of a popular hit melody, Lee tapped a string sandal in time with the pulsing beat. In spite of herself her gaze strayed to-wards Drew. Apparently he was deep in conversation with a group of young sheep farmers. Lee reflected that the men employed by him on the station had given her to understand he was a man who drove him-self relentlessly day and night and was utterly absorbed in his work. Maybe he had never taken the opportunity to learn to dance—or wasn't interested. The next moment she realised he was striding purpose-fully across the floor in her direction. 'Dance?'

They moved together on a floor slippery with the oil of a thousand fleeces. Drew was an expert dancer, Lee realised, matching her steps to the intricate move-ments his feet were performing. He never ceased to surprise her, this man she thought she hated.

The pop music crashed to a close and Lee was turn-ing aside when the musicians broke into an old-time melody and she found herself caught up in Drew's strong arms as he whirled her away to the lilting rhythm of *The Tennessee Waltz*. Over the wild tumult of her senses she told herself, It won't hurt to pretend, just for tonight, that he's a different man, as wonderful as he looks. Just this once I'll forget everything else and give in to that strange attraction that, why not admit it, he has for me.

All too soon the dance came to an end and Drew led her to a chattering group. Lee caught a fleeting glimpse of John's open young face, his expression dark and brooding. The next moment she found herself meeting Katrina's resentful glance. 'Seems tonight's Polynesian night,' Katrina's lips curved scornfully. 'Don't tell me that Drew bought a dress for you too when you were over in Samoa with him?'

'No,' Drew said unsmilingly, 'I had nothing to do with Lee's shopping in Samoa,' and excusing himself, he left the group to join a knot of men standing further down the big room.

A little later, dancing with David, Lee caught a glimpse of Katrina and Drew among the crowd on the floor. Katrina was looking animated and happy, her smiling face uptured to his.

As the evening wore on Lee decided that Drew could take his choice of partners. He danced many times with a tall, striking-looking girl with a magnificent coil of fair hair. Evidently, Lee mused, he preferred his girl-friends to be blonde. All at once a masculine voice nearby said breathlessly, 'Made it!' and she swung around in astonishment. 'Paul!'

'Thought you'd be surprised.' He looked inordinately pleased to see her.

Indeed she scarcely recognised in the immaculately dressed young man with carefully slicked down hair, her helpful dish-drier of last week's harrowing days in the woolshed. 'Where did you come from?' she asked.

He laughed. 'A hundred miles or so—but no matter, the thing is I'm here.' His face glowed with pleasure. 'And you're here. Heck, to think I nearly missed out! I only heard about the dance at the last moment. I've never got cleaned up so fast in my life. It was just too good a chance to miss.'

'You like dancing so much?'

'I like *you*! On top of that I had transport problems,' he went on as he led her on to the dance floor. 'The car had a flat battery and I had to beg a lift with some of the gang.' He laughed. 'We sure had a full truck by the time we got away.'

'Good for you!'

His gentle smile warmed her heart. 'It was worth it all, to see you again.'

Lee flashed him a teasing smile. 'Bet you tell that to all the shearing-gang cooks!'

They danced together again and again. Once she partnered David, then Paul was immediately back at her side. Lee didn't mind. It was nice to be with a man who appreciated her company for a change, instead of being either carping or angry with her as Drew was all of the time—well, most of the time.

Paul was about to claim her once more when Drew cut in, 'Mine, I think!' and before the other man had time to argue the matter, Drew had swept her away.

Lee felt a traitorous happiness rising in her like a burst of sunshine on a dull day and because she didn't want to feel that way about Drew she said defensively, 'You don't have to dance with me, you know, just because——' something in his deep compelling glance froze the words on her lips and she finished in a low tone, 'if you don't want to!'

'Who's complaining?' She scarcely recognised him in this gay lighthearted mood. 'Not me,' he said with an exultant grin, and led her away.

From time to time she was aware of Katrina's watchful glance, but the other girl had no need to concern herself about Drew and herself, she thought wryly.

The pale glow of pre-dawn lightened the eastern horizon when at last the musicians packed away their instruments and couples began to drift away from the dance floor. Lee, flushed and breathless, stood for a moment with Paul. She was only half aware of his eager tones, her gaze fixed on Katrina, who had been dancing with Drew. Her glance moved to John, standing alone in the shadows.

'Now that I've found you,' she wrenched herself back to Paul's tones, 'don't think I'm going to let you go. I'm giving you fair warning, Lee.'

She smiled. 'I don't see how——'

'I'll manage it somehow. I won't be on the shearing circuit for ever, and there are telephones.' He threw a hurried glance towards a group of burly men who were headed in his direction. 'Hell, we're off already! If only I had my own bus. I'll have to get cracking right now. Next time,' he pressed her hand, 'I'll make sure I have my own transport, then I can say goodnight to you the way I want to—Okay, I'm coming!' With a last lingering glance he turned away to join his workmates.

Lee realised that the shed was emptying. The two young shepherds and their wives paused to throw her a 'goodnight' before they too went out into the darkness. Lee followed them down the steps, but she could see no sign of the party from the homestead and after a moment's hesitation she decided to stroll back to the house. It was only a short distance, after all.

She had reached the start of the curving driveway when she caught the sound of a vehicle behind her. The next moment a Land Rover slowed to a halt at her side and Drew leaned from the driver's seat. 'Why didn't you wait for me?' He sounded, Lee thought, as though he were back to his usual domineering self. 'I've been looking for you all over the place. I was only away from the shed for a few minutes. Mum was in a hurry to get back, so I ran her back to the house first.'

'It's all right,' she said with what dignity she could muster. 'I'm nearly home now.' She glanced up at him, hoping he wouldn't notice she had spoken of his house as 'home'. 'I thought you'd all gone and anyway——'

'You'd better get in!' He flung open the passenger door and because she felt a little foolish standing on the empty driveway arguing over such a trivial matter, she decided to do as he asked, commanded rather. So she climbed up the high step of the vehicle.

Drew drove in silence. To her surprise, he didn't pause when they reached the front entrance but swung the Land Rover down a path leading to the orchard. He pulled up in the shadow of some overhanging trees, then swung around to face her. Lee drew a quick breath. Now what?

'I wanted a word with you.' For the second time that night she caught the suppressed excitement in his tone. Could it be the dim light of the dashboard that lent his dark face an expression of tenderness? Her pulses gave a betraying leap and just in time she recalled his habitual disapproval of her. Drawing a deep breath, she forced her tone to one of long-suffering patience.

'You're angry with me because of my taking on the job of looking after your aunt here at the house. It's the very last thing in the world you want me to do, isn't it?'

'If you really want to know,' he drawled in his infuriating way, 'I'm darned pleased about it. It couldn't have happened at a better time. Best news I've had in a long time!'

'What?' She stared up at him, eyes wide in astonishment. He was smiling, even in the gloom she could see that. Not his usual variety of the lift-of-the-lip grimace but a warm, honest-to-goodness smile.

'You don't believe me, do you?'

'I——' Lee didn't know what to say. 'It's a bit difficult after what you told me about not wanting me to take on that sort of work. And now, with your aunt, in your home——' She broke off, then said slowly, 'Tell me, what made you change your mind . . . about me? I can't believe,' she added wryly, 'it was my outstanding ability as shearers' cook that made the difference.'

'You put up a whale of a performance, did a great job.' Lee could scarcely believe this conversation was for real. 'But no, that wasn't it.'

How many times had she longed to hear just those words of appreciation from his lips? Yet now when the miracle had happened she could feel nothing but bewilderment.

He said very low, 'I guess this might come as a surprise to you,' he covered her work-worn paw with his big brown hand, 'but I owe you an apology.'

His touch started a trembling in her, but she nerved herself to say suspiciously, 'Since when?'

'Since this, actually. It arrived by the mail van yesterday.' He had taken a letter from his pocket. 'It's from my sister in Samoa.' He took a flashlight from the shelf of the vehicle and spread the blue notepaper beneath her gaze. 'You'd better take a look. It explains quite a lot.'

Lee sent him a puzzled glance, then dropped her gaze to the handwriting illuminated in the light of the torch he was holding.

'Just a request for information, brother, as there's something I'm rather curious about, or someone, rather, a girl by the name of Marquand. The day I saw you off at the airport here I remember there was a girl with you in the car, someone you called Lee. Well, it's the strangest thing, but the British Consulate have been making enquiries on the island about a girl named Lee Marquand. Seems the kid had a pretty rough time while she was here. According to the superintendent of a nursing home in England where the girl used to work, she came out here as a sort of nurse-companion to the most difficult and domineering woman the staff had ever had on their hands. Seems this unpleasant woman had approached the other girls working in the convalescent home, but they turned down her offer, knowing how impossible she was to deal with. The Matron was of the opinion that the girl Lee had a kind heart and would be just the person to take on the trip, thinking she was doing the tyrant a good turn.

'Anyway, the elderly woman, who happens to be immensely wealthy by the way, took ill and collapsed in the street almost as soon as they arrived in Apia. She admitted to the Matron that she sent the companion away for a drink of water, but a passer-by whisked her away to hospital before the girl could get back. The story the woman told the hospital staff at the time was that the companion had callously deserted her, but that wasn't true, she admits now. She's evidently frightened of the consequences as it seems she left the girl Marquand with no money and no way of getting back to England (they'd had single fares). She's only admitted what really happened now because the girl seems to have disappeared without a trace. The last anyone saw of her was when she stayed on for a day at Aggie Grey's hotel.

'Now, I couldn't help wondering though if your Lee and this missing girl are the same person, but I won't say a word until I hear from you. The Matron in London is quite concerned about her whereabouts, so if you can throw any light on the mystery, could you let me know as soon as possible? Meantime, must go. Lots of love. Bev.'

Lee felt a great surge of relief, as though a tremendous weight had lifted from her shoulders. She felt as light as air and happier than she had been for ages. Aloud she asked, 'So what are you going to do?'

'Tell the authorities the truth, of course.' He added, very low, 'And make my apologies to you. I guess I was all wrong about you Lee.'

'It's all right.' Lee smiled. She could smile for ever now, she thought happily. How many times had she dreamed of this scene, and now it was coming true!

She became aware that he was eyeing her narrowly. 'Of course you know what this means?'

'Well——'

'Either the superintendent of the nursing home will want to lend you the money for your return fare to England or your old employer who did you so much harm will have got the wind up with all the bad publicity over at the other end. You can bet your life she'll be only too happy to pay for your air ticket back to London, if only to square things on her account. Folk like her don't take kindly to being caught out in a shady deal like the trick she played on you back in Samoa.'

The thoughts were tumbling through Lee's mind in wild confusion, for she knew he had spoken the truth. So what was she going to do? All at once she knew quite well what her answer to the offer would be. She said clearly and decisively, 'No!'

'*What?*' Drew was regarding her in astonishment. 'I thought you wanted to get back to England more than anything else in the world?'

'I do, I do! But not that way! If I borrowed the money from Matron I'd be ages paying it back and I'd feel—oh I don't know, under an obligation to her. After all, I should have had money in the bank for the fare home myself. If it hadn't been for——' she broke off in some confusion. Thinking aloud got you into unexpected difficulties, like almost letting on about Jeremy to whom she had entrusted her savings and who had let her down badly. Another person whom she had naïvely trusted, to her cost. 'The thing is,' she went on in a low constrained tone, 'that I want to get back by my own efforts, not by means of a hand-out. I couldn't bear to accept the fare money from Mrs Cartwright, not after what happened.'

'I get it.'

Suddenly a dismaying thought crossed her mind. By burning her bridges she had made herself once more dependent on Drew and he had already made it plain that he had no intention of permitting her to work elsewhere than here at his home. True, he was being most affable at the moment, but that no doubt was only because he had been forced to admit he had made a serious error of judgment regarding herself. She couldn't imagine this unfamiliar friendly Drew lasting. She was right, she thought the next moment as she caught the triumphant expression in his eyes.

'So it all comes back to your working for me?' He threw her a quirky grin. 'Even though that's the last thing you want to do?'

Driven to retaliation, she threw back at him, 'I haven't much option, have I, if I want to be independent?'

'Suits me.' All at once he was gay and lighthearted.

All at once she was torn by conflicting emotions. There was something about Drew in this unfamiliar mood that was undermining all her preconceived convictions about him. The way she was feeling, in another minute if she stayed here with him—'I'd better go in,' she said breathlessly, 'the others will be sending out a search party for me.'

He took not the slightest notice. 'They'll know you're with me—besides, there's something else——'

'Something?' She raised startled blue eyes.

'Don't argue, Lee!'

Before she could make an answer she found herself enfolded in his arms, caught close, close against the muscular hardness of his chest. Then his lips found hers and everything went flying from her mind as her senses were set afire by the wild sweetness of his lingering kiss. Time ceased and there was only the magic of his nearness. Abruptly he released her. 'You'd better go.' His voice was oddly hoarse. Then without another word he started the motor and drove back to the entrance steps.

As they made their way in silence along the hall he was as remote as ever, Lee thought, just as if nothing world-shattering had happened out there in the stillness of the dawn. Maybe in his view, nothing had happened. At the foot of the stairs he left her with a brief, ''Night, Lee.'

Slowly she went towards her bedroom. From the lounge room below she caught echoes of talk and laughter punctuated by the chink of glasses. She could hear Katrina's high sweet voice, caught the sound of Jean's merry laugh and the deep timbre of men's voices, but she wished only to be alone, to try to puzzle out the events of the night. It was wonderful to think she had been vindicated at last in Drew's estimation by the letter he had received from his sister in Samoa, but a matter of even greater significance tugged at her mind.

In her room she dropped down to her bed, thinking, thinking. She could still feel Drew's kiss burning on her lips and her thoughts milled in confusion. Why,

why had he done that? It was quite out of character. A gesture of apology, because he hadn't believed her story of what had happened in Samoa? Or could it be because she was a new face in the district? If there was one thing she had learned since coming here it was that girls were scarce in the outback. Did he really like her? Almost she could have imagined—— Or had his kiss been a mere nothing, something to be regarded as no more than the boss's privilege? Somehow it was important that she know the answer, for Drew's kiss had shaken her more than she cared to admit.

Presently the tramp of men's boots on the path below drew her to the window. A sunburst of vivid flame was spreading over the horizon and in the dawn light she caught a glimpse of Drew and David, changed now into their working gear of cotton shirts, work shorts and heavy boots as they went towards the Land Rover for the start of their day's work.

She stood by the window for a long time, watching the vehicle move down the winding track, and all the time the wild excitement persisted, and with it the questions to which there seemed to be no answers. Did Drew really like her after all, or had it been just a kiss?

CHAPTER EIGHT

As the days went by, however, Lee decided that the kiss that had shaken her world had been a matter of little moment to Drew, probably no more than a passing impulse, and she had best put the memory from her mind—if she could.

Katrina's friend John had stayed on to take part in the local hunt to be held on the station, and it seemed to Lee that Drew's family and employees talked of nothing else.

'Drew and I never miss the opening hunt,' Katrina told her. Even if we happen to be miles away from here—somehow we'll both get back in time for that!' Why must Katrina speak in that proprietorial fashion about Drew, Lee wondered irritably, as if they were two people with the same interests—or two people in the stage of a budding love affair? She shook the thought away, realising that the other girl was regarding her with one of her impish glances that more often than not, held a hint of malice.

'Pity you don't ride well enough to join in with the rest of us,' Katrina was saying, 'but you're so handy in the catering department. You'll be able to give Mrs Mac a helping hand with getting the goodies ready for the breakfast at the end of the day. Or maybe you could come along with the oldies and follow us from the hills by car.'

'Don't worry about me,' Lee set her lips in an endeavour to bite back the angry retort that rose in her mind, 'I've got lots to do tomorrow anyway.'

Katrina raised innocent blue eyes. 'Such as?'

Lee produced one of her careless smiles. 'Tell you when I come back!' for Mrs Mac was beckoning her from the doorway.

'Telephone for you, Lee.'

Presently she forgot Katrina's edged remarks, for Paul's voice, ringing with warmth and sincerity, came clearly over the line. 'Lee? If I'm not glad to find you at home today! How are you?'

'Fine! Just fine!'

'Gee, it's good to hear your voice.' Then, in a rush of words, 'Look, I've got a few days to spare between shearing dates, so how about coming over to stay for a few days at our place, starting from tomorrow, when I'll come and collect you?'

She said hesitantly, 'But isn't it a long way for you to come?'

He said incredulously, 'When we can have three days to ourselves? You'll like my folks,' she imagined he was running on so as not to give her a chance to refuse his invitation, 'so long as you don't take any notice of my sisters. There are two of them and they might give you a bit of a time.'

'Why would they do that?'

'Well,' he sounded embarrassed, 'I don't often bring a girl home.'

Something in his tone gave her the impression that he had never before taken a girl-friend to meet his family. 'Do you think I'd better risk it?' she said laughingly. 'What if they get ideas about us?'

All at once a serious note tinged his tone. 'I wouldn't mind. Lee——'

'Anyway,' she broke in before he could say anything further on the subject, 'I'll take you up on that invitation.' Because Katrina's mocking words still niggled at the back of her mind she added, 'I'd love to come—I really would!'

'Tremendous!' Paul seemed unable to believe his good fortune. 'I'll be over to pick you up tomorrow, early. Bring your bikini with you. There's a pool and a tennis court, if you're interested.'

'Oh, I am!' She had a sense of satisfaction in the thought of being able to join in activities that she was accustomed to, not like hunting—— She pulled her thoughts up short, realising that at the other end of the line Paul was laughing softly.

'You do sound enthusiastic. Don't tell me you're an expert swimmer or a crack tennis player?'

'No such luck. But I enjoy a game of tennis, and your pool sounds fabulous.'

'I'll order some extra sunshine just for you,' he promised.

'Bribery will get you nowhere!'

When Lee replaced the receiver in its cradle she turned to find Katrina regarding her curiously. 'Who was it?' Katrina enquired with assumed indifference.

'Just a friend.' Lee had no intention of letting on to Katrina her plans for the weekend.

'Oh,' the other girl's small mouth drooped peevishly as she turned away, 'I can guess anyway.'

'Why ask, then?'

Lee stared after Katrina's departing figure, her gaze abstracted. There was no reason at all why she shouldn't pay a short visit to Paul and his family. The woman she had promised to look after here wasn't due to leave hospital for a week and she was sure that Jean would be anxious for her to see another part of the country. As to Drew . . . if he had shown the slightest interest in her she knew she wouldn't be planning to be away from Mahia this weekend. It was maddening to have to admit it, but she knew that if he felt differently towards her, as at times she had mistakenly imagined, she wouldn't be able to drag herself away.

She might even settle for following the hunt tomorrow just for the sheer pleasure in watching Drew take the fences.

Presently she wandered down towards the stables where she found Jean checking her gear in readiness for the morning's hunt. When she told the older woman of her invitation to another station for a few days, Jean looked up in surprise from her task. 'It's fine with me, Lee, a good chance for you to get around the district a bit—but have you told Drew about this?'

'Drew?' Lee was puzzled. 'What do you mean?'

'Nothing, nothing. Just that I got the idea he had something planned for you on Saturday.'

'Oh!' Lee felt a chill sense of regret, then she pulled herself together. Probably, she mused derisively, he had ideas of asking her to help with the hunt breakfast. Big deal! Why should Drew care whether she went or stayed? He had his 'kitten', didn't he—and that, she reflected on a sigh, was all he really cared about.

That evening after dinner when the other men sauntered away in the direction of the pool table, Drew went out to the verandah and came to stand beside Lee. She was leaning over the railings as she watched a great ball of fire sinking over the horizon.

'Coming to watch the hunt tomorrow, Lee?' he asked, and without waiting for her answer, 'Could be a new experience for you—or have you seen it all before, back in England?'

'No, I've never been to a meet.'

'This will be your chance, then. Some of the staff are going along by car to watch. I'll jack it up for you to go with them.'

'Don't bother.' She lifted her gaze to his and immediately came under the battery of his penetrating gaze that, for some reason she couldn't understand, always had the effect of unnerving her. Now is the time, she reminded herself, to take revenge on this man. *Act assertively*, she scolded herself. Aloud she said, 'Sorry, but I've promised to go away this weekend.'

The silence seemed to last for ever. At last she said in a flurry of words, 'It's Paul. He's got a few days free of his shearing stint and asked me if I'd come and stay at his home for a few days.'

'I get it.'

She darted a quick glance towards him and was surprised at the set line of his jaw. What had she said, for heaven's sake, to make him have that grim expression? He was coldly furious, she could see it in his eyes. Strangely she felt no elation in the knowledge that somehow she had managed to interfere with his plans, only that niggling ache of regret.

'You didn't want me for anything this weekend?' she felt constrained to say. 'Because if you did——'

'*Want* you?' He bent on her his deep disturbing look and she felt a tide of colour run up her cheeks. 'My dear Lee,' she wondered wildly how could a man's eyes be so chilly and at the same time burningly alive, 'whatever gave you that idea?'

The thoughts ran wildly through her mind. So they were back once more to the old antagonism that sparked between them. The brief madness on the night of the woolshed dance might never have taken place. He *couldn't* have meant anything by that kiss! 'Your aunt——' she grasped at the first thing that came into her mind, 'I wouldn't go away this weekend if there was any likelihood of her needing me——'

'There isn't.' His cool dispassionate tone was discouraging. 'You're perfectly free to please yourself.'

She said with what composure she could muster, 'If by any chance your aunt is discharged from hospital earlier than she expects, you will let me know?'

'Don't worry Lee, no one's all that indispensable.'

At the irony in his tone her cheeks burned hotly. Of all the hateful, sarcastic men! She was glad, glad, glad that she was leaving Mahia, if only for a few days.

The next morning she watched from the creeper-covered verandah as horse-floats and stock trans-porters assembled on the flat ground by the stables. There seemed to be a steady stream of vehicles still arriving. Newly-clipped horses were being saddled and riders were pulling on their jackets. Jean looked up from the people she was talking to and waved to Lee. 'Have a good time! See you when you get back!'

Lee was scarcely aware of the words, because at that moment Drew, accompanied by a radiantly happy Katrina, hurried down the steps. At the sight of him Lee drew a sharp breath—she couldn't help it, for wearing white nylon breeches, the dark green of his hunting jacket setting off his black hair, he looked more devastating even than she had imagined.

'Goodbye, Lee.' He shot her a cool glance.

She was still on the verandah a short time later, watching as the field set off towards the first paddock behind the hounds, when a late model car rounded the bend and drew up at the verandah steps.

Paul took the steps two at a time, then hurried to-wards her. He caught her in his arms, then dropped a kiss on her small tanned nose. 'I didn't think I'd be so lucky——'

She laughed. 'Why ever not?'

'I don't know.' The laughter in his eyes died away. 'I guess I thought you'd have something else on.' His tender glance rested on her face. 'A girl like you.'

'Well, I didn't,' she said crisply, and had a sudden tormenting thought. What had Drew had in mind for her at the weekend, had she stayed here? If only she knew! If only she hadn't allowed Katrina's spiteful remark to spark her into leaving the station.

'Something wrong?' She became aware of Paul's anxious look. 'Not having second thoughts, are you?'

'No, no, of course not!' She produced one of her brilliant smiles. She would need to watch her expression, she told herself, for evidently Paul was more discerning than she had given him credit for. 'I'll fetch my bag,' she said lightly. 'Bikini, you said? Tennis gear? That's a bit difficult for me. Tops and shorts, will they do?'

He nodded happily. 'Sure will. Anything goes at our place, so long as you come!'

'Give me two minutes!'

A quick word of farewell to Mrs Mac and soon Lee was seated at Paul's side in the car. As they reached the top of the hill a high wind from the sea tossed her curly hair back from her forehead and sent the waves crashing up on the glinting black sands below. Ahead of her lay a pleasurable day in a novel environment, yet somehow she couldn't wrench her thoughts away from Drew—and Katrina. She was a girl who could match him at clearing the highest fences, she talked his language.

'I've got a few things planned for you.' Paul's pleasant tones broke across her musing. He flashed her a shy sideways smile. 'For us.'

'Nice! What did you have in mind?'

'Nothing spectacular. A few outings——'

'Everything here is different to me. I come from England, remember?'

'Are you a town or country girl, Lee?'

'Town, so far.' She laughed. 'But I'm learning fast. Since I came here I've even learned to ride a horse—if it's guaranteed to be quiet. The plodding kind, that's for me.'

'I've got just the mount for you, so if you'd care to go riding with me——?'

'Love to.'

'Right, it's a deal! You know something?' He grinned. 'For a townie you're coming along fine!'

'It's all the tuition I get. Ernie's going to put up some higher jumps for me to practise on. He——' Her voice trailed away as she caught a glimpse of a group of riders who were clearing a high barbed fence running across a slope. She had no difficulty in recognising Drew's erect back, and close on his heels came Katrina, who else? For a time she lost the thread of Paul's discourse. What was he saying? Something about the 'old man' . . . 'wants me to take over the place in a couple of years, he's had a lot of back trouble lately and thinks he'll have to take things easier in the future. That's why I'm working on the shearing circuit, there's a helluva lot to learn.' He laughed. 'Especially as I'm fairly new to the game. I've been living in town putting in some study in architecture. It was always understood that my elder brother Bill would take over the station when Dad decided to step down, but what did Bill do but marry an Australian girl and go farming over there! His wife doesn't want to live in Kiwiland, so I guess now it's up to me to give it a go. The old man's got it all worked out that in a year or two he and Mum will move down to one of the cottages on the property and I'll take over the big house and all the rest of it. I've got two sisters, both at training college this year, but they'll be away teaching before too long.'

Lee said thoughtfully, 'But won't the house be too big for you?'

'That's all part of the five-year plan. By that time I'm supposed to have found myself a wife. I wasn't very interested in that part of the project—until now.'

'There's lots of time,' Lee said cheerfully, 'to think about that. You might have half a dozen girls you fancy in all that time.'

'One will do me.' A depth of feeling tinged his tone. 'So long as it's the one I want.'

It was ridiculous, she thought, for him to think that way about her. Aloud she said laughingly, 'Don't look at me! You scarcely know me.'

'Don't I?' The car slewed to the side of the road as he turned to look at her and at the same moment a great stock transporter thundered past, a cloud of dust rising behind it.

'Sorry,' Paul swung the steering wheel around, 'but it's all your fault. I was looking at you.'

'The road might be safer,' she said drily, as he pulled up before a narrow bridge to allow a stock truck to go by.

They were leaving the coast behind them now, taking a metal road cutting between green slopes. Ahead Lee could see no sign of civilisation, only green, sheep-threaded hills with their dividing fences of tall macrocarpa pines, the bush-filled gullies below, and the silence.

The sun was high in the sky when at last they came in sight of a white-gabled homestead nestling among towering evergreen trees.

'It's a lovely old home.' Lee leaned forward in the seat, looking towards a sprawling white-painted timber house with a blue roof built on a hilltop.

'Not bad.' She caught the note of pride in his voice. 'It's not as vast as Mahia. I'll be able to handle it all right with a few shepherds to give a hand with the mustering. Mum's wrapped up in gardening,' he volunteered, as they swung off the road and took a winding driveway. Indeed, as they neared the homestead Lee's gaze took in a sweep of clipped green lawns studded with flowering shrubs, oleanders, proteas, the scarlet Australian waratah and the flaring pink blossoms of Suva Queen hibiscus. Here, she realised, was quite a different set-up from the sheep station she had left. There were well tended tennis courts, the blue waters of a great pool were screened by overhanging bushes, fences were freshly painted a shining white. So why did she feel this ache—not homesickness, surely— for Mahia with its high winds and rugged coastline, and its master? . . . its master. Drew, his hair as black as the scintillating iron-sands, his enigmatic smile. Arrogant, masterful and devastatingly attractive. Why couldn't she get him out of her mind?

It was easier to forget that disturbing man, she found, once they arrived at the homestead. Paul's sisters ran to the small gate to welcome them and soon they were leading her over a creeper-hung porch and into a long hall. 'We're just longing for someone young to talk to!' Dianne, a pretty fair girl who looked very much like her brother, hooked her arm in Lee's.

'Especially anyone from England,' her sister Annette, merry and red-haired, put in smilingly. 'Di and I are saving up to go to London once we get through training college!'

All the way down the long hall they plied her with eager questions about life on the other side of the world. London—the people, the fashion scene, the shows. Lee could scarcely keep up with the stream of enquiries.

'For heaven's sake, girls,' Paul's mother came to greet Lee, 'let her get her breath before you drive her mad with your talk!' Mrs Forrest, an energetic little woman with bright brown eyes, was as friendly as her daughters, and when at the midday meal Paul's father, a tall rather frail-looking man, took her hand in his, Lee decided that she really liked Paul's family.

Later that day, however, she was feeling slightly overwhelmed by the attentions of the two girls. While the sisters carried on a spirited argument as to whether

Lee would prefer a game of tennis to a dip in the po⌐
Paul drew her aside. 'Still want to go for a ride?' h⌐
whispered.

'Can't wait!'

'Come on, then. Gently does it. We'll have to give
them the slip.'

Lee gave a brief thought to the jeans and cotton top
she was wearing, rubber thongs on her feet—but no
matter, they would have to do. Silently she and Paul
crept down a narrow path at the back of the house, to
emerge near the stables. Paul caught the two horses
and only a short time later he and Lee rode out of the
gate and into a grassy paddock.

'You might have waited for us!' Lee caught the
shouted message and turned to see Dianne and Annette hurrying towards them. 'We're coming anyway!'
Paul shouted back.

'No, you're not! Give me a break, you two. Lee'll
ride with you tomorrow.'

'So you say! Promises, promises!'

But the two girls turned back the way they had
come, and Lee began to understand what Paul had
meant when he had spoken of his sisters as some sort
of a problem. They overwhelmed one with kindness.

Breakfast the next morning was a gay and informal
meal with everyone talking at once, and Lee found
herself treated as one of the family. Paul, his warm
gaze fixed on Lee's face, announced calmly and decisively, 'It's no use you all making plans for Lee
today. I'm taking her to the races at Matakauri.'

'We'll make up a party!' Dianne suggested anim-
atedly.

'No, you won't! No one asked you two to come
along,' Paul grumbled, and Lee began to understand
his feelings regarding her being 'taking over' by his
family. 'Must you come?' he groaned.

'Of course we're coming too,' Annette put in. 'You're not the only one here who likes a day out.'

Over the clamour of dissenting voices Paul's mother raised her eyes heavenwards. 'You see how it is, Lee! I suppose this is what comes of being a close family.'

'Close!' Lee caught Paul's low angry mutter. 'It's more like a stranglehold, I'd say!'

A little later, however, seated at the wheel of the long, dust-covered car with Lee at his side and his two sisters in the back seat, Paul appeared to have resigned himself, Lee thought, to sharing the outing with his family. Two hours later they swung through the entrance gates of a racecourse. A little later they were in the members' stand and idly Lee leafed through her race book. She knew nothing of the racing world and indeed had rarely attended a meeting.

When the time approached for the next race, Lee joined with the rest of the party in putting a small amount of money on a local horse, and as the hooves pounded the soft earth of the track, people all around them got to their feet, shouting the name of their favourite. The horses swept past the barrier in a mass of heads and hooves and it wasn't until the numbers flashed into sight on the totalisator that Lee and the others knew their horse had been the winner.

'A good start for the day,' declared Paul. 'From now on we can't lose.' It was, however, a prophecy doomed to failure, for as the hours wore on any modest winnings that came their way were swallowed up in losses.

Lee didn't really care about the dividends. She was enjoying the carefree atmosphere of this small country meeting that had made the hours fly by like magic. Suddenly she became aware of a voice over a loud speaker announcing the final race of the day. The last race! Suddenly a wild and reckless mood possessed her, and with it came the thought that if she placed quite a large sum of money on the Quinella, a strange word that she now knew meant betting on two horses to come first and second in the same race, if she held the winning tickets, *then* wouldn't she have the edge on Drew! He would no longer control her life, force her to stay at his home *under his terms*. She would be free at last of his dominating influence, able to return to England whenever she liked.

As if in tune with her wild imaginings two names leaped up to her gaze from the race book she held in her hand. 'Samoan Princess' and 'Opportunity Knocks'. Who could resist the implications?

Why not? She knew now what she was going to do.

She waited in line at one of the boxes and before she had time to change her mind pushed a wad of notes towards the man behind the glass barrier.

As she pocketed the slips, Paul came hurrying towards her. 'What did you fancy?'

'Aha!' she laughed, 'it's a secret. Tell you later if I'm on a winning streak.'

Back in the grandstand with the others, she could barely bear to watch as the line of horses sprang away from the starting barrier and came pounding around the track. 'Anything Goes is in the lead,' Paul was telling her excitedly, but she scarcely heard him, her gaze fixed on the big bay and the small black mare, both scarcely discernible among the cluster of horses. The field was still the same when the horses had completed the circuit. 'Last time around!' Paul yelled in her ear, for now the crowd had risen, and everyone was shouting the name of their favourite. Then all at once the deafening roar of the crowd died away and in the silence Lee saw Opportunity Knocks, closely followed by Samoan Princess, sweep on to pass the winning post.

'Wow!' Paul turned an astonished face towards her. 'What a race! Hey!' He gazed at her in surprise. 'You look as though you've collected the winning divvy or something, sort of . . . stunned.'

'I'm all right.' She tried to pull her thoughts together. This was the moment for her to admit her luck in holding the winning tickets, yet something held her silent. For one thing, she shied away from the publicity that would be inevitable once the identity of the Quinella winner became known. 'I'll tell them when we get home,' she promised herself, and went with Paul to join the crowd of people lining up at the 'pay' counter, to all intents for the purpose of collecting a small dividend on a third winner. In the queue she found herself separated from the party and the attendant behind the counter showed no particular interest in the large sum of money he was handing to her. She was feeling a little light-headed. It had really happened, the once-in-a-lifetime miracle she had scarcely dared to hope for. Now the door was wide open for her to escape from Drew. Why, he held her almost a prisoner in his home. But not any longer! She couldn't wait for the moment when she told him that she was free to come and go as she pleased.

The next moment she looked up to find herself gazing directly at him.

'Why,' he grinned his infuriating grin, 'if it isn't the girl from Mahia!'

Not any longer, she told herself, and suddenly she found it the easiest thing in the world to smile up into his mocking eyes. The trouble was, she never could hold his gaze. It did things to her, sent everything flying from her mind except his nearness. She dragged herself back to sanity. 'Aren't you a bit late for the meeting?' she enquired coldly. 'The last race is just over.'

'I didn't come here for that—come with me, Lee.'

He put a hand on her bare arm and she felt herself tingling at his touch on her warm skin.

Together they leaned over the railings. 'Why *did* you come?' she challenged him.

'To collect you, actually.' He was wearing his enigmatic smile.

'*What?*'

'Just what I said! I had to come over to get you— now don't look like that. I'm not planning to abduct you. I thought I'd be fairly certain of finding you here today.'

She asked curiously, 'What did you want me for? It must be something important to bring you all this way.'

'Sure is! Remember that nursing job I jacked up for you?'

'You mean looking after your aunt?'

'That's the one. Well, it seems the hospital are turfing her out earlier than arranged. The old girl's made such good progress they're of the opinion she can get on fine now at home,' he bent on her his deep compelling look, 'providing she has someone at hand to keep an eye on her. I told her doctor there was no problem. She'll be sure of just as good care at home as in the ward. That way,' he went on blandly, 'there'll be a spare hospital bed going for someone else. I told him we'd pick her up tomorrow.'

Now was the time for her to let him in to her newly-found independence. And yet, the thought niggled at the back of her mind, she had made him a promise and nothing altered that, not even the matter of her unexpected winnings.

She realised he was watching her with his disturbing glance. 'Tonight, you mean?'

'Now, actually. I've come to take you home, Lee.'

She thought the words had an odd significance. Not

that he meant what she was thinking, of course, far from it.

'What's the trouble?' His penetrating look was hard to meet. 'Having too good a time here?'

'It's just——' she hesitated, 'Paul won't be very happy about my taking off like this. He's looking forward so much to having me around tomorrow——'

'So is Aunt Edith,' Drew reminded her coolly, adding as if that put an end to the argument, 'and she damn well needs you!'

All at once his bland assumption of her compliance with his demands sent a shaft of anger through her. You're no longer dependent on this man, she reminded herself, and burst out defiantly: 'This might come as a surprise to you, but I don't *have* to do as you say!'

'No? You did promise,' he reminded her relentlessly, 'to give the old girl a hand.'

'I know, I know.' She caught her lower lip with her teeth. He had used the one argument she couldn't deny, darn him!

'Couldn't you get someone else?' she enquired coldly. 'Maybe you'd find someone with more qualifications.'

'At a few hours' notice? Not a hope! You're way off beam when it comes to knowing about employing trained nursing staff in the district. Besides,' she distrusted the wickedly triumphant gleam in his eyes, 'the old girl refuses to consider anyone else, insists on you and no one else.'

She looked at him suspiciously. 'You must have done a great job of building me up, then.'

'Oh, I did! You'd be surprised! That's why I knew you wouldn't let her down.'

What could she do? she thought helplessly. She would never square her conscience if she failed to keep her word. If only he didn't have that self-satisfied glint in his eyes. She glanced towards the rest of the party, now moving away from the pay-out booth. 'I'd better tell the others I'm leaving.'

He nodded. 'We can pick up your gear from the house on the way.'

At that moment Paul and his sisters came to join them and it was Drew who briefly explained the situation.

Paul took the blow well, Lee thought, only a tightening of his lips betraying his disappointment at the curtailment of Lee's visit. His sisters' arguments and pleas for Lee to stay for just one more day died away. Plainly, Lee thought, the two girls realised from Drew's flint-hard expression that entreaties were useless. He was a man who meant business.

Back at the homestead the family gathered in the driveway to bid her goodbye. Paul's family joined in a warm invitation for her to return just as soon as she had a weekend free from her duties with the injured woman who was to be in her care. Paul said nothing. He had no need to ask her to come back, Lee thought, his firmed mouth and stricken expression said it all. She was still turning back from her seat in the Land Rover to wave to her new friends when a curve in the winding driveway swept the group from view.

CHAPTER NINE

ALL at once she was swept by a wild sweet happiness there was no accounting for. Something to do with the remoteness of the scene maybe? How about *finding herself alone with Drew*? the goblin in her mind jeered.

Catching his sideways grin, she imagined there was a look of downright satisfaction in his eyes. Well, pretty soon she would change all that. Before long *she* would be the one to wear a triumphant expression!

'You can take a run back here some other time,' the deep careless tones broke across her musing. Did he mistake her quietness for resentment because of the interrupted holiday break? she wondered.

'I guess so. Annette and Dianne were sorry I had to rush off in a hurry like this. They were counting on me to fill them in on the London fashion scene——'

'It wasn't the girls I was thinking of.'

'Oh, Paul?' she laughed, 'he'll get over it,' and wondered at the sudden light that had leaped into his eyes.

'Bring your swimming gear with you?'

Now it was her turn to be startled. 'Yes, I have. There was a super pool at Paul's home.'

'I can take you to a better place for a swim than any pool. We can get a swim anywhere along the coast and the water's warm after a hot day like this. How does that strike you?'

It struck her as a perfectly wonderful idea, but she had no intention of letting him know that. 'Sounds like fun,' she said quietly.

They went on, taking steep, grassy hills climbing to meet a cloud-filled sky and with every mile that fell away behind them Lee felt a deepening of her sense of content.

His voice intruded on her musing.

'How do you like being a farm girl anyway?'

'Love it.' She spoke unthinkingly.

'That should give Paul some encouragement!' There was a tense note in his tone that she couldn't fathom.

'Paul?'

'Don't pretend you don't know what I'm getting at!' he said harshly. In one of his swift changes of mood he was back to his old overbearing self, interfering with her life, *taking over*. 'Any fool can see the way things are going with you two!' He flicked her a sardonic glance.

'I thought you liked him,' she said coldly.

'What's that got to do with it?'

Really, she thought, he had no right to delve into her personal life! Could it be the knowledge of the wad of notes hidden in her bag that lent her this new feeling of independence? She said defiantly, 'I know I have to work for you, but that doesn't mean that you own me!'

'Unfortunately.' The word was grated out in so low a tone that she wondered if she had misheard it, for after all, 'fortunately' would sound very much the same. She threw him a sideways glance and was surprised at the tight set of his lips.

They went on in silence and it was some time later when Lee roused herself to say, 'I can smell that salty tang of the sea. We must be nearly home!' and knew a subtle pleasure in the word 'home'.

'That's right.' They were swinging into a rough track winding down to the coastline below. Drew braked to a stop and Lee looked around her. At each end of the sweep of bay high cliffs fell sheer to the tossing waves below. The sun, setting in a fiery ball on the western horizon, sparked a myriad flashing lights in the ironsands.

He came to stand at her side. 'You're looking at the Tasman Sea. Not exactly your idea of a golden South Pacific beach, I take it?'

'Not really.' She smiled. 'But it's got something, I don't quite know how to put it—a remoteness! Her gaze swept a succession of bays lost in a mist of sea-spray in the distance. 'No one but ourselves in all these miles of beach!'

Drew said softly, 'Do you mind?'

She felt a stab of piercing sweetness. 'Not a bit! It's a novelty. I——' Her voice trailed into silence as she found she could no longer sustain his deep compelling look.

'Lee——' As she raised her eyes he stepped towards her and the next moment, as if by instinct, she found herself nestling in his strong arms. She could feel his hard muscular chest against her soft body, then her senses were swept out of control and there was only his nearness and strength and the heady elation of his mouth on hers.

'Hell!' She was jolted roughly back to reality as he set her free and, senses swimming, she realised that two men in wet suits seated in a large rubber dinghy were guiding their craft towards the line of surf on the choppy sea.

'I thought you said,' Drew murmured on an angry breath, 'that we had the place to ourselves.'

For Lee, however, nothing could dim the moment of his kiss. Right now she didn't question the depth of his feelings for her. Her senses still rioting in a wild happiness, it was enough that he too had felt that in-escapable attraction between them, as natural as the pull between moon and sea.

They stood in silence, watching the craft now approaching the curling breakers. The men aboard the dinghy waited a few moments, then, using oars, came inshore on the crest of a wave that carried them into the shallows. A few minutes later they were hauling their craft up on the sand. A brief salute sketched in the air to Drew and Lee, then the skin-divers moved towards their waiting tractor and soon they were lost to sight on a bend of the winding track.

'Well,' Lee raised a flushed face to his, 'what was all that about?'

Drew's voice was still tinged with resentment. 'A couple of skin-divers. They've been checking the pipe from the cliffs taking sand underwater to the Japanese boat out there at sea.'

'Oh, well,' she told him with a smile, 'we've got the beach to ourselves again.'

'That's the way I like it,' he said softly, 'so long as I'm with you.'

She could scarcely believe this was the boss speaking. The warmth of his tone, the tender, sort of special way he was looking at her—it was like a dream. She made an effort to control her whirling thoughts and for something to say, asked, 'Didn't you tell me you had something to see to down here in the bay?'

He flicked her an enigmatic grin. 'Two reasons for coming here, actually. One's confidential, but the other is that I've got to bring in the kon-tiki——'

'Kon-tiki?' Lee echoed bewilderedly.

'My way of fishing—a little raft with baited hooks. See that little sail way out beyond the breakers?' He was very close as he indicated an area beyond the reef and as always his nearness was working its magic with her so that she had difficulty in concentrating on the tiny craft she could glimpse bobbing among the waves. She forced her mind back to his words. 'I've been waiting all week for an offshore wind and on my way to collect you today I swam out with the kon-tiki to take it beyond the breakers. With a bit of luck we might have a catch. Let's take a look, shall we?'

Her hand in his, they moved along the beach towards a reel standing on the sand and he began to haul in the line. Soon the little raft was riding the waves to skim inshore and even before it splashed through the foaming spray Lee caught the silvery gleam of fish.

'Ever tasted schnapper freshly caught from the sea?' Drew, with the speed of long practice, was scaling and skinning the fish.

She shook her head. 'But I guess there's always a first time.'

'A swim first,' he declared, 'then dinner!'

'A swim in this sea?' Lee's gaze went to the waves dashing in a cloud of spray against the rocks at the end of the bay. 'Isn't it a bit—dangerous?'

'Depends.' He glanced up from his task, the corners of his lips curving in secret amusement. 'Not in the way you mean.' At something in his expression she decided not to pursue the subject.

Presently he strolled to the Land Rover to come back with her bag. 'Changing sheds are over thataway,' he indicated a jagged black rock nearby. 'Meet you in two minutes!' He moved away towards the shadowed cliffs, damp swimming trunks swinging from his hand.

Lee just had time to change into her black bikini before Drew, tanned and lean and muscular, came striding towards her.

'Come on!' He clasped her hand in his and together they ran into waters that were flooded with the gold and flame of the rays of the setting sun, to be met by pounding surf that plunged Lee beneath the waves. But she didn't mind being half drowned, she reflected, not when it meant being carried to shore through the breakers, safe in Drew's strong arms.

When at last he set her gently down on the sand, she squeezed sea-water from her hair and asked a trifle breathlessly, 'What's around the next point?' Her gaze was on a rocky outcrop at the end of the curving bay.

He said carelessly, 'Nothing very exciting. More iron-sand, more driftwood, cliffs——'

'I'm going to take a look!' She turned and sped away, only to find that progress was difficult on the heavy wet sand. He caught up with her in no time at all and she found herself held fast in his arms. She looked up laughing into his face.

'It's no use your running away, young Lee,' she caught his words over the roar of the surf. 'You'll never get away from me!'

'Never?' she said lightly, but her heart was beating unevenly.

'I'm warning you!' He dropped a kiss on her small sun-tanned nose, then drew her back along the sand. The warmth of the sun still lingered as they strolled back towards the reel on the beach.

Soon Drew was arranging stones on the sand, piling dried brushwood in a heap on top. 'This is a do-it-yourself-job.' He set a match to the brushwood and flames soared high in the clear air. Lee dropped to the sand, hands linked around her knees and eyes on the flames. 'Want me to get a pan from the Land Rover?'

He nodded. 'It's on the back seat.'

While he gathered driftwood and laid it on the flames she came back from the vehicle with a cardboard carton that she set down on the sand. 'Seems we've got all the essentials, one blackened billy, one frypan, tinned milk, sugar and tea bags, oil.'

'That's all we need!' He was placing the pan on the stones, heating the oil. This time, Lee marvelled inwardly, it wasn't the shearers' cook who was preparing the meal, but the boss himself!

She had to admit, however, that as a chef he

couldn't be faulted. Could it be the firelit scene so far from familiar surroundings that lent the food a melt-in-the-mouth quality? Even the tea, served in enamel mugs, was deliciously thirst-quenching.

Afterwards he moved away to gather more drift-wood, piling it high until the flames danced and soared against the darkening sky. Then he came to drop down at her side, propping himself on an elbow and looking up into her flushed face. His eyes glimmered in the dusk and once again her heart began its uneven beat. It was the way he affected her, a physical thing, she told herself, against which she found herself powerless.

'What would you say,' she forced herself to concentrate on his deep soft tones, 'if I told you I'd made a special trip to bring you back with me tonight?'

Her pulses seemed to leap and settle again. 'But I thought your aunt was arriving from hospital to-morrow and you—needed me.'

'*Need you!*' His voice was husky. After a moment he went on, 'No, the patient's being discharged from hospital in the afternoon. We could still have made it if I'd picked you up in the morning.'

She tried to subdue the tumult of feelings rioting through her by picking up a handful of sand and sifting it through her fingers. 'Why did you, then?' she asked.

'Just wanted to get you to myself for a change, settle a few things I've had on my mind——'

'Such as?'

'This!' In a swift movement he had drawn her to him and as his seeking lips found hers Lee felt the world spin out of orbit. Her senses were swimming and she was finding it difficult to keep her head—and that was something she must do, because he was the boss and there were things he should know. When at last she could speak she said shakily, 'I've got something to tell you——'

His arms fell away from her and his expression hardened. 'Paul? Are you saying that you and he——'

'No, nothing like that!' Beneath his penetrating gaze she was finding difficulty in choosing the right words.

'Well then,' he was lighthearted once again, 'it can't be anything very important.'

She hesitated, the thoughts flying wildly through her mind. This was the moment she had waited for, when she would let him know that she was no longer the 'biddable little thing' that circumstances had made her appear to him in the past. She was her own woman, and if it wasn't for the hammering of her heart she would be cool and collected enough to tell him in no uncertain terms—— It was no use, something deep inside her betrayed her, for when once again he moved to take her in his arms there was nothing in the world but his kiss. He took his time about it and when at last he released her she was trembling.

He said very low, 'Why are you trembling, Lee?'

She turned her face aside, said in a muffled tone, 'Why do you think?' She had been kissed before, of course, but never before had she been aroused to feelings that all but submerged her, sending her emotions as alight as the flames rising against the darkness around them. In an effort to keep some hold on her runaway emotions she groped her way back to sanity. She had planned to put her story so concisely, to revel in her triumph over him, yet now she heard her own voice making a bald statement. 'Something happened to me today at the races. I was lucky enough to win a Quinella. I put my money on two horses that I picked just because of their names—Samoan Princess and,' she hesitated, then went on in a rush, 'the other one was called Opportunity Knocks. Anyway, they came in first and second place and I collected a lot of money, more than enough to get me back to England.'

'I get it,' there was a tight note in his voice. 'Opportunity Knocks! What am I supposed to offer you, congratulations or commiseration?'

She looked up into his set dark face. 'Why—commiseration?'

'I think you know the answer to that one,' he rasped. 'You'll stay on with me, of course?' He was back to his old autocratic self, she thought indignantly, very much the master of a vast holding in this outback community. Really, she might just as well not have set herself free of his domination. She said very low, 'I don't have to.'

'No, you don't have to, but you will!'

It was too much to take from him. 'Who says so?' she flared.

'I do! Come on, Lee,' he drawled persuasively, 'you're a country girl now, a natural. What else would you do?'

'Go back to hospital work——'

'Not you! Not now!'

'I could——'

'But you won't. You'll stay on at Mahia.'

'Because you tell me to?' Her heart was pounding wildly. At last she said the words she had rehearsed so often in her mind. 'I don't have to do what you say any longer.'

'Look at me, Lee!' He had her neatly. He knew quite well, darn him, he had known all along that she weakened under that magnetic masculine gaze. So she took no notice but went on letting the sand slip through her fingers. 'Of course,' she schooled her voice to a light and carefree note, 'I'll stay for a while, until your aunt doesn't need me any longer.' Feeling more in command of the situation she added, 'I did promise, and I'm a girl who always keeps her word, remember?' An unaccustomed sense of freedom and power was going to her head and she added teasingly, 'I might just stay longer, if you ask me the right way.'

'My way?' Before she could answer, he had taken her in his arms. 'Lee, Lee my darling——' She caught the murmur of his voice, then the warm sweetness of his lips on hers sent her into a world of heady rapture.

When at last he released her, he looked into her flushed face. Holding her at arm's length, he said softly, 'Well, do I get my way?'

She said unsteadily, 'I guess you've made your point.'

Could it be the firelight that made his eyes seem deep pools of shadow? 'You don't sound too sure about it. I've got arguments I haven't put to you yet, so if you like——'

'No, no,' she said breathlessly, 'I'll stay.'

Drew was silent for a moment, then abruptly he turned away. 'I'd better take you home,' he said in an odd husky tone.

While he threw sea-water over the glowing embers, Lee gathered together mugs and pan, tossing them into the carton. Then she went away to change back into jeans and cotton top.

Back in the Land Rover with Drew's arm thrown around her shoulders as they took the dark hills, her thoughts drifted. Thank heaven, she mused as they sped on in the darkness, he had no inkling of the tumult of emotion his nearness, let alone his kisses, aroused in her. Never before had she felt this way when a man had kissed her. But this wasn't any other man, this was Drew!

When they reached the homestead, except for a lantern shining on the verandah, the house was in darkness. At the foot of the stairs they paused together and he raised a hand to run it lightly down her soft cheek.

'Goodnight,' his lips brushed her mouth, 'see you in the morning,' then he turned away.

A little later, lying in bed and looking up through the uncurtained window at a sky dusted with stars, Lee wondered if she had ever before seen stars so brilliant. Or was the sparkle only in her own mind, exploding like a shower of light whenever her thoughts drifted back to Drew? It was then that it hit her like a blow. She was in love with him, crazily, deeply, hopelessly. And he? A shiver of delight went through her. Tonight he had seemed to like her a lot and maybe if they carried on from tonight ... It was morning before sleep claimed her.

CHAPTER TEN

LEE awoke with a delightful sense of well-being. Then
memory, flooding back, brought with it the warm feeling of being loved. Not that Drew had put the thought
into so many words, but the way he had kissed her, the
caring note in his voice, spoke for him. She couldn't
wait to be with him on the long journey into town
today. Just the two of them. For somehow she felt sure
he wouldn't welcome anyone else on the trip, not after
the magic hours they had spent together last night on
Sunset Beach. Idly she considered her wardrobe, but
it didn't really matter about clothes, Drew wouldn't
care what she wore, so long as they were together. The
thought came with a deep sense of content.

A little later when she reached the dining room she
found it empty. The men would have breakfasted earlier and the rest of the family hadn't yet appeared. No
matter, Lee hummed a tune under her breath as she
mixed instant coffee and switched on the toaster.

She had all but finished the light meal when Katrina
came into the room, exquisitely dressed in a white
pleated skirt and an emerald green blazer, her blonde
hair hanging loose around her face. 'Don't worry
about me,' she told Lee gaily, 'I've had all I want to
eat ages ago. Drew is a stickler for my being bang on
time when we take off for town together!' Something
of Lee's look of blank surprise must have got through
to her, because she said laughingly, 'Oh, Drew wanted
me to go with him to town today.' Perching herself on
the edge of the table, she swung a foot clad in a high-
heeled white shoe, 'That's why he went haring after

you yesterday to bring you back in time. He didn't want me to be stuck with the job of looking after his aunt until he got back. Drew's so thoughtful. He wouldn't let me in for that. He knows how I loathe anything to do with sickness.' She pushed the shining blonde strands back from her ears. 'Besides, he wanted us to have some time in town together before he had to pick up his aunt.'

'He went to Paul's place to get me,' Lee echoed slowly, 'because of you?'

Katrina looked surprised. 'Of course. Drew always thinks of me first of all, he's like that. He just wouldn't stand for me having to do anything I didn't want to, especially chasing after an invalid who can't do things for herself.'

As if becoming aware of Lee's stricken expression she added a little selfconsciously, 'Of course it's different for you, being a nurse and all that—I'd better get my bag.' She drifted out of the room.

A chill passed slowly, slowly through Lee's body. So it was all a fantasy on her part. Last night's magic, born of firelight and a dark beach, was a nothing thing, no doubt already put from Drew's mind now that he had achieved his purpose. To think she had actually believed that he had sought her out for romantic reasons! She must have been crazy to think such things. He had other more important matters to think of, she mused bleakly, like escorting Katrina around town. She had a mental picture of the other two in the car on the long trip over the hills, his dark head inclined towards her, an expression of amusement on his face as he listened to her childlike prattle. Well, if that was what he wanted ... Then, on a sigh, if only it didn't hurt so much!

A moment later she caught the tread of heavy footsteps outside and presently Drew came striding to-

wards her. Freshly shaven, the thatch of black hair on
his forehead still damp from a shower, he had about
him an aura of masculinity and vitality. His glance
went straight to Lee and he was smiling, she thought,
as if he had the whole world at his feet, as no doubt
he had in a way. He had his 'kitten', didn't he,
not to mention another silly girl who had been easily
taken in by firelight and soft words and a few light
kisses.

'All set for the big excursion today?'

She looked away from his too-perceptive eyes. 'I'm
not coming,' she said flatly.

'*What!*' All the good temper faded from his expression and his eyes blazed into hers. 'Why not?'

Lee managed a light shrug of her shoulders. 'I've
changed my mind about the trip today, that's all. I
thought I'd be more use here, getting your aunt's
room ready for her and all that.'

He came to tower over her. 'That's a lie and you
know it! You're coming with us, Lee!'

It was the 'us' that sent her angry thoughts spinning
out of control. 'I don't have to——'

'Do what you tell me?' His dark face wore a cynical
smile. 'Isn't that what you were going to say?'

'Something like that,' she said very low.

'Right, if that's the way you feel about it!' He flung
around to see Katrina standing in the doorway, her
bright alert glance moving from Drew's furious expression to Lee's strained features. 'At least *you'll* be
on hand today to give Aunt Edith a hand on the way
back!'

Katrina twinkled up at him. 'You know you can
always depend on me, Drew.' They left the room together.

Stupid of her, Lee thought, tears pricking at the
back of her eyes, to feel this way. She had always

known that Drew liked his cousin—correction, second cousin; there was quite a difference, come to think of it, but it wasn't until this moment that she realised just how much. She stayed at the window for a long time, staring out unseeingly, and it wasn't until the Land Rover vanished from sight around a bend in the hilly track that she turned away. The blow had been so sudden that she felt numbed by it. Yet the anguish she was feeling was her own fault, she told herself, for allowing herself to fall in love with a man whose feelings were all for another girl. Even at this moment he was out enjoying himself with his little cousin.

Strange how life could deal one such a shattering blow, yet to outward appearances nothing seemed changed. Only Jean, coming in to the room at that moment, looked surprised. 'Lee! I thought Drew was taking you with him today to the hospital to collect Edith. You decided not to go?'

'That's right.' She turned her head aside to avoid Jean's clear gaze. 'I thought I'd stay here and get things ready for her when she arrives.'

'You shouldn't have worried. Mrs Mac's busy sorting out sheets and pillowcases.' Jean's voice had a puzzled note.

In an effort to vindicate herself for what must appear to Jean downright negligence, Lee explained, 'I thought your aunt would be all right on the journey. I mean, she'll have Katrina to help her.'

'Hmmm.' The older woman did not appear to hold a high opinion of Katrina's nursing capabilities. She was taking in Lee's strained appearance, the freckles standing out against the pallor of her face. 'You're not feeling well——?'

'Yes, yes, I'm fine.' Once again Lee avoided Jean's discerning gaze. 'I'm looking for a job—if you have one?'

Jean still looked unconvinced. 'Well, if you really want one there's the little table out in the shed. You could give it a polish and set it by the bed in the spare room. Oh, and some flowers—Edith's a great gardener in her own home.'

'I'm on my way!' Lee was only too glad of any task that would take her thoughts from Drew and Katrina. She polished the old kauri bedside table until it gleamed, then gathered roses, asters and delphiniums from the flower borders, arranging the blossoms in a blue bowl. She placed her own little gilt travelling clock on the mantel and flung open the long french windows to let in the fresh salt-laden breeze from the sea.

Jean, coming in a little later, glanced around her approvingly. 'It looks bright and welcoming, don't you think? Edith won't have to be in bed for very long, another week or two, then she'll be up on crutches. She's such an active little person I can't imagine her in bed for two weeks, but she'll be sure to have lots of things to amuse herself with. She's one of those women who are always off on some new hobby. She must have been through most of the handcrafts by now and the funny thing about it is that she seems to make a success of each one.'

'Goodness!' But Lee wasn't really listening. Her thoughts were with Drew and his 'kitten', together on the long trip into town, enjoying the start of their day together. She wrenched her mind back to Jean's voice. What was she saying? Something about Katrina. 'Drew wouldn't get away from here without Katrina. She adores a day's shopping in town.'

Lee thought, *She adores Drew.*

Jean seemed to tune in on Lee's unhappy musing. 'She clings to Drew. Have you noticed?' *Had she noticed?*

'She really thinks the sun shines out of him.' *Don't we all?*

'But of course you can understand the way she feels about him——'

Oh yes, I can understand only too well. Lee was only half aware of Jean's voice.

'Deep down she's a loving little thing and there's good reason for that sharp tongue of her. She's a bit bitchy sometimes, I know, but when you understand the cause ... You see, she adored her father, she's an only child, of course, and when he died and her mother married again she took it hard. She was so jealous of her stepfather it was quite ridiculous! Everyone in the family thought she would grow out of it, but that was all two years ago and she still takes every opportunity she can to get away from her own home and over here. It's a sort of father fixation.'

Is that what you call it? thought Lee. Because it hurt too much to discuss Katrina and Drew, she made the observation silently. How little people really knew of one another's lives, she thought on a sigh, even those who lived a close family life as was the case at Mahia.

Never had she known a day to drag by so slowly. The invalid's room was fresh and airy, sweet-smelling with the roses in the vase. A water jug and glass stood on the low table. Writing materials and a selection of light novels were placed ready to hand. Even the bed, with its lilac floral cover, was turned down in readiness for Aunt Edith's arrival.

Restlessly, not knowing how to fill the hours, Lee wandered down to the stables. Maybe, she thought listlessly, she would go for a ride. A canter over the ridge and along the grassy sweep of the airstrip was surely enough to make one forget any problems that bedevilled the mind. *Not this one.*

She wandered on down to the stables where she found Ernie, his white head bent over the shoe he was hammering to the hoof of her mount. 'If you're wanting a ride,' he told her cheerfully, 'this won't take long . . . steady there! Just a loose shoe.'

'There's no hurry.' She dropped down to seat herself on a box nearby.

'You didn't go into town with Drew today?'

'No.' She raised her heavy glance to his weathered, lined face. Drew. Dreadful to have to admit to herself that in spite of her letdown she couldn't stop herself thinking of him, talking of him. It was as if she couldn't hear enough of him. 'You think a lot of him, don't you?' she hazarded.

Ernie took a horseshoe nail and hammered it into place on the mare's shoe. 'You can say that again! He's one of the best, if you know what I mean!'

Lee did, for even her brief acquaintance with the Kiwi male had taught her that Ernie wasn't one for effusion and to these country men a few well-chosen words could convey a world of meaning. She pretended, however, to ignorance. 'You mean he's a good boss, knows his job, looks after his staff?'

'*Knows his job!*' Ernie stared at her incredulously. 'Put it this way. It's pretty well known on all the stations that any man who's got his training under Drew is dead certain of a job on a sheep farm anywhere in the whole country!'

'But surely there must be other men of the same calibre around?'

'Ain't ever met up with them myself.' He selected another nail. 'No, he's out on his own, is Drew. Top polo-player, world-class at show-jumping championships all over the globe, and when it comes to knowing his job, there's no one to match him. David now, he's a decent enough young bloke, works well enough so long as Drew's keeping an eye on him and telling him what to do, but he'll never be the man his brother is. He just hasn't got it in him.'

'A man's man! But he was all set to be married once, wasn't he?' Dangerous ground, this, but Lee couldn't resist the temptation to talk about him. 'When was that, two, three years ago?'

'Must be all of three years now. All for the best, maybe, though he took it hard at the time.'

'How do you mean?' she asked.

Ernie shrugged broad shoulders. 'It wasn't all plain sailing for those two, not by a long shot! All water under the bridge now, so it won't matter my telling you that for a start, she was a good bit older than Drew, a concert pianist from overseas who happened to be touring the country when she met up with him. She didn't take kindly to the prospect of settling down on a sheep station in the back of beyond. The engagement was broken off a couple of times, I daresay for that reason, and anyone could see there were fireworks ahead for them. She just wasn't cut out for country living.'

Lee couldn't help the query that sprang to her lips. 'And ever since there's been no other girl for him?'

Ernie sent her a friendly wink. 'Not until he got back from that last overseas trip.'

His meaning was all too clear, and it hurt. Not since he had come to realise that his 'kitten' was no longer an amusing youngster but an alluring young woman?

Ernie's shrewd gaze was on Lee's downcast face. 'Fallen for the boss yourself, have you?' His friendly chuckle robbed the words of idle curiosity. 'Can't say that I blame you.' His faded eyes held an expression of real caring.

It was the expression on his weathered face that trapped her into speaking the truth. The words came without her volition.

'Stupid of me, isn't it? You'd think I'd have more sense than to do a thing like that!'

'Can't help these things,' Ernie shrugged philo-
sophically, 'There,' he got to his feet, 'that's the job
done. Like me to saddle her up for you?'

'Please.' She spoke absently, because what did it
matter where she went today or what she did, always
there would be the ache of longing and letdown.

Ernie had helped her up to the saddle when she said
on a sigh, 'I'm going to miss all this when I go.'

'Go?' There was a note of genuine concern in his
voice. 'You're not leaving us?'

'I'm afraid I have to.' She was unaware of the wist-
fulness that tinged her tone. 'I'm looking after
someone called Aunt Edith for a while, but she's expected to be up on crutches in a couple of weeks and
then,' in spite of herself her voice broke, 'I guess that
will be it!'

'Sorry to hear that.'

Ernie scratched his white thatch of hair thoughtfully. 'I thought maybe you and Paul, that young
bloke who's always hanging around here, might have
ideas——'

'Paul?' Her indulgent tone said a lot. 'Oh yes, he's
nice, but——'

'Nice? Is that all you can say for him? I was hoping
he might be able to keep you in this part of the
country,' he winked significantly, 'one way or another.'

'I think he's got plans——'

'But you're not interested?'

Lee shook her head. 'No, I've got to go.'

He sent her a puzzled glance. 'You don't seem too
pleased with the idea. Must you——'

'Yes, I must. I'll tell you a secret,' somehow she
could never lie to Ernie, 'I'm going to miss everything
about the station. I'll never forget you, or Jean either,
or the girls down in the bungalows.'

'How about Drew and Katrina?'

'Oh yes, Drew . . . and Katrina.' In spite of herself her voice thickened and she turned her head aside to hide the tears that misted her eyes. 'I'd better get on my way. Goodbye.'

'So long, Lee.' He stood looking after her as she took the winding cliff path, his gaze thoughtful. 'So that's the way of it!' he muttered. 'She doesn't know for sure, she's jumped to conclusions, taken it as gospel that Drew and that young cousin of his . . . She could be wrong about that, dead wrong. She could give it away and be sorry for the rest of her life. I've got half a mind to shove in my car and put it to Drew, though if I'm on the wrong track he won't thank me for interfering!' Suddenly a light of resolution shone in his eyes. 'But she's worth taking a risk for, is Lee, the nearest thing to a daughter that I'll ever have, and if she were mine I'd give it a go!'

Half an hour later, out on the hills where the wind was blowing, Lee let the mare pick her way down the track. Far below she glimpsed the tossing seas and swirling black sands of Sunset Beach. The wildness of the scene matched her restless mood. Last night . . . Lost in her heavy thoughts, at first she was unaware that she wasn't alone on the windy slopes, then, borne faintly on the wind, she caught the sound of her own name. 'Lee! Wait!'

Glancing back over her shoulder she caught sight of a horseman approaching at a gallop and swiftly narrowing the space between them. Drew! There was no mistaking his lean erect figure. And she had imagined him to be fifty miles down the main road—with Katrina. Why was he following her? It couldn't be anything of importance, and if he imagined he had merely to shout her name and she would meekly wait for him . . . Suddenly the feelings boiled up inside her. Drew, who had made her love him and to whom she was merely a diversion. The blood surged through her veins in a mood of reckless abandon. She would show him that she had learned something else at his sheep station besides the hopeless loving she had for him. He had told her not to take the high jumps—and he was fast gaining on her!

All at once the first fence loomed ahead, the barbed wire running horizontally across the steep slope. She would prove to him she was no longer just the shearers' cook but a girl to be reckoned with, a girl who could beat him at his own game! The wind was singing in her ears as she neared the jump and for a desperate moment, as the mare stumbled, Lee was in danger of being thrown, but Gypsy regained her balance just in time and Lee set her at the high fence. As she landed on the other side she thought jubilantly, Now there's only one to go! Behind her she could hear the sound of hoofs on the turf and knew that Drew had made the jump too and was now almost on her. But she was in the lead for the jump over the second fence. Crouching low in the saddle, she felt the mare lift in the air, clearing the dangerous barb. Over! But she had congratulated herself a moment too soon, for as her mount landed on the other side the mare twisted at an angle and before she knew what was happening, Lee found herself tossed down the slope.

She rolled over and over for a short distance, then picked herself up, dusty and dishevelled, to find Drew hurrying towards her. His face was thunderous. 'Why didn't you stop when I called to you?'

But she was done with subterfuges. She brushed the hair from her eyes and moved to the mare, standing motionless, the reins trailing on the grass. 'Why should I?'

'For heaven's sake, girl,' his eyes were blazing in a

pale face, 'don't you know you took your life in your hands taking those fences? Those sort of jumps are for experienced riders only.' He eyed her narrowly. 'You're not hurt?'

She shook her head, then brushed the dust from her T-shirt and examined a graze on her elbow. 'That's what I'm doing, getting experience.'

His eyes were cold steel. 'For what? Looking after old ladies in a rest home?'

She faced him, eyes bright with defiance. 'Maybe.'

'You won't, you know.' His tone was dangerously quiet.

'Why not?' Something in his tone started the trembling in her.

'Because I won't let you go! Because you belong right here with me. Why do you think,' he added softly, 'that I sent David off in the car today to fetch Aunt Edith? It was *you* I wanted with me.'

There was a mesmerism about him, she thought, there must be, for she was in his arms, his hand tilting her rounded chin. 'Look at me Lee, and tell me you still want to leave.'

He was holding her close, her curly head nestling beneath his chin. 'I didn't ever say,' her voice came muffled, 'that I *wanted* to go away!' All at once she flung caution to the winds, because what did anything matter now but cold truth. She looked up to meet his compelling gaze. 'I thought that you—and Katrina——'

'You thought *what*?' The words came on an incredulous breath. 'Are you telling me that you got into your head that she and I——? She's just a kid, a nice kid, who looks on me as a sort of father figure. I thought you'd have tumbled to that long ago or I'd have spelled it out to you. The way I feel about you——' His voice was husky, then his words were lost as his seeking lips found hers. 'I tried to tell you once,' he murmured a little later, 'but I had the idea then that Paul and you——'

Lee drew herself a little away as a thought came to her. Flushed and smiling, she sent him a suspicious glance. 'You didn't see Ernie a little while ago, did you?'

'What if I did?' Gently he traced a hand down her soft cheek, brushing away a smudge of earth.

'I just wondered,' she said in a burst, 'if he told you about me.' His grin was tender. 'Just enough to get him invited to the wedding——'

'You haven't asked me,' she dimpled, 'and I just might say no.'

He kissed her full on the lips. 'You might, but you won't!'

It was happening all over again, she thought with a quiver of delight. Only now they were arguing *on the same side*. It was a novel sensation and deeply satisfying. She decided that she didn't after all mind that Ernie had betrayed her confidence.

Drew seemed to read her thoughts. 'Don't hold it against Ernie,' he said softly, 'for giving me what I want!' Once again his seeking lips found hers and it was some time before Lee could concentrate on his deep tones, husky with emotion. 'You must have known I was crazy about you.'

Face flushed and eyes bright with a newly-discovered happiness, she shook her head. 'I know now, and that's all that matters!' She twined her arms around his neck. 'I love you, Drew.'

Masquerade
Historical Romances

Intrigue excitement romance

CHANGE OF HEART
by Margaret Eastvale

Edmund, Lord Ashorne, returned from the Peninsular Wars to find that his fiancée had married his cousin. It was her sister Anne who had remained single for his sake!

LION OF LANGUEDOC
by Margaret Pemberton

Accused of witchcraft by Louis XIV's fanatical Inquisitor, Marietta was rescued by Léon de Villeneuve — the Lion of Languedoc. How could she *not* fall in love with him, even knowing that he loved another woman?

Look out for these titles in your local paperback shop from 13th March 1981

The Mills & Boon Rose is the Rose of Romance

Every month there are ten new titles to choose from — ten new stories about people falling in love, people you want to read about, people in exciting, far-away places. Choose Mills & Boon. It's your way of relaxing:

March's titles are:

GREGG BARRATT'S WOMAN by *Lilian Peake*
Why was that disagreeable Gregg Barratt so sure that what had happened to Cassandra was her sister Tanis's fault?

FLOODTIDE by *Kay Thorpe*
A stormy relationship rapidly grew between Dale Ryland and Jos Blakeman. What had Jos to give anyone but bitterness and distrust?

SAY HELLO TO YESTERDAY by *Sally Wentworth*
It had to be coincidence that Holly's husband Nick — whom she had not seen for seven years — was on this remote Greek island? Or was it?

BEYOND CONTROL by *Flora Kidd*
Kate was in love with her husband Sean Kierly, but what was the point of clinging to a man who so obviously didn't love her?

RETRIBUTION by *Charlotte Lamb*
Why had the sophisticated Simon Hilliard transferred his attentions from Laura's sister to Laura herself, who wasn't as capable as her sister of looking after herself?

A SECRET SORROW by *Karen van der Zee*
Could Faye Sherwood be sure that Kai Ellington's love would stand the test if and when she told him her tragic secret?

MASTER OF MAHIA by *Gloria Bevan*
Lee's problem was to get away from New Zealand and the dour Drew Hamilton. Or *was* that her real problem?

TUG OF WAR by *Sue Peters*
To Dee Lawrence's dismay and fury every time she met Nat Archer, he always got the better of her. Why didn't he just go away?

CAPTIVITY by *Margaret Pargeter*
Chase Marshall had offered marriage to Alex, simply because he thought she was suitable. Well, he could keep his offer!

TORMENTED LOVE by *Margaret Mayo*
Amie's uncle had hoped she would marry his heir Oliver Maxwell. But how could she marry a maddening man like that?

The Mills & Boon Rose is the Rose of Romance

THE STORM EAGLE by *Lucy Gillen*
In other circumstances Chiara would have married Campbell
Roberts. But he had not consulted her. And now wild horses
wouldn't make her accept him!

SECOND-BEST BRIDE by *Margaret Rome*
Angie would never have guessed how the tragedy that had
befallen Terzan Helios would affect her own life . . .

WOLF AT THE DOOR by *Victoria Gordon*
Someone had to win the battle of wills between Kelly Barnes
and her boss Grey Scofield, in their Rocky Mountains camp . . .

THE LIGHT WITHIN by *Yvonne Whittal*
Now that Roxy might recover her sight, the misunderstanding
between her and Marcus Fleming seemed too great for anything
to bridge it . . .

SHADOW DANCE by *Margaret Way*
If only her new job assignment had helped Alix to sort out the
troubled situation between herself and her boss Carl Danning!

SO LONG A WINTER by *Jane Donnelly*
'You'll always be too young and I'll always be too old,' Matt
Hanlon had told Angela five years ago. Was the situation any
different now?

NOT ONCE BUT TWICE by *Betty Neels*
Christina had fallen in love at first sight with Professor Adam ter
Brandt. But hadn't she overestimated his interest in her?

MASTER OF SHADOWS by *Susanna Firth*
The drama critic Max Anderson had wrecked Vanessa's acting
career with one vicious notice, and then Vanessa became his
secretary . . .

THE TRAVELLING KIND by *Janet Dailey*
Charley Collins knew that she must not get emotionally involved
with Shad Russell. But that was easier said than done . . .

ZULU MOON by *Gwen Westwood*
In order to recover from a traumatic experience Julie went to
Zululand, and once again fell in love with a man who was
committed elsewhere . . .

If you have difficulty in obtaining any of these books from your
local paperback retailer, write to:

Mills & Boon Reader Service
P.O. Box 236, Thornton Road, Croydon, Surrey, CR9 3RU.
Available April 1981